Editor: Robin Robertson

Firebird 3

Writing Today

Pe

Penguin Books Ltd, Harmondsworth, Middlesex, England
Penguin Books, 40 West 23rd Street, New York, New York 10010, U.S.A.
Penguin Books Australia Ltd, Ringwood, Victoria, Australia
Penguin Books Canada Ltd, 2801 John Street, Markham, Ontario, Canada L3R 1B4
Penguin Books (N.Z.) Ltd, 182–190 Wairau Road, Auckland 10, New Zealand

This selection first published 1984

Made and printed in Great Britain by
Richard Clay (The Chaucer Press) Ltd, Bungay, Suffolk
Filmset in Monophoto Sabon with Univers display by
Northumberland Press Ltd, Gateshead

Contents

Acknowledgements

'Leaf Memory' copyright © Elizabeth Baines, 1984

'Memories of the Space Age' first published in *Interzone* 1982; copyright © J. G Ballard, 1982

'Zerlina' and 'Leporello' first published in *Oxford Poetry* 1983; copyright © David Constantine, 1983. All other poems copyright © David Constantine, 1984

'The Liberation' copyright © Alasdair Gray, 1984

'A sook fur freedom' copyright © Alex. Hamilton, 1984

'Facing North' and 'Cypress & Cedar' first published in *The Times Literary Supplement* 1983; copyright © Tony Harrison, 1983. 'Flood' and 'Aqua Mortis' first published in *Encounter* 1983; copyright © Tony Harrison, 1983. All other poems copyright © Tony Harrison, 1984

'The Giant Christ on the Road to Marsalforn' copyright © David Harsent, 1984

Six Poems by Michael Hofmann copyright © Michael Hofmann, 1984

'Alan's Novel' copyright © Desmond Hogan, 1984

'Above Laggan' first published in *The Gregory Awards Anthology 1981 and 1982* (Carcanet); copyright © James Lasdun, 1982. 'On the Road to Chenonceaux' first published in a limited edition by Giles and Jonathan Leaman 1982; copyright © James Lasdun, 1982. All other poems copyright © James Lasdun, 1984

'End of Season' copyright © Bernard Mac Laverty, 1984

'The Game at Ghost Beach' copyright © J. New, 1984

'The Irish Signorina' copyright © Julia O'Faolain, 1984

'To Him Away' first published in *Straight Lines* 1980; copyright © Jeremy Reed, 1980. 'Christopher Smart in Madness' first published in *Temenos* 1982; copyright © Jeremy Reed, 1982. 'Buoys' first published in the *Literary Review* 1983; copyright © Jeremy Reed, 1983. All other poems copyright © Jeremy Reed, 1984

'The Silence of the Land' copyright © Keith Roberts, 1984

'Casualty' copyright © Richard Thornley, 1984

'After Veronese's "Susannah and the Elders"' copyright © Marina Warner, 1984

'Pterodactyl' copyright © Paul Winstanley, 1984

Elizabeth Baines

Leaf Memory

ELIZABETH BAINES was born in South Wales in 1947 and read English at University College of North Wales, Bangor. Her stories have appeared in anthologies and magazines (including *Bananas*, *Stand*, the *Literary Review*, *Encounter*). Her first novel, *The Birth Machine*, is published by The Women's Press.

*T*his is the memory:

Down below is a brown dry stream. It swishes. One long unbroken swish: that's the wheels; and slumph-slumph: that's Nanny's feet. I put my arm over the side – bluish-black, with a bright white line that slides along slyly when I move my head. I lean right over. I put my hand down into the stream, and the dry bits tickle.

'Put your hand in,' says Nanny.

I sit back on the cushions.

Nanny's hands are on the handle. Between them, another line of light winks and glares.

The dry things swish.

One gets stuck in a wheel. Clutter-clutter. I look over. It whips, round and round. It flickers on the others.

Where do they come from?

'From up,' says Nanny.

The trees are up. Up there it is green, green and black against the sky.

'They fell off,' says Nanny. 'The brown ones fell off.'

She is starting to puff. Now we've begun to go up the hill. I slide forward. My feet press on the bottom.

Crackle-crackle in the wheels. The colour of burn. The burnt ones fell off.

The burnt bits are down.

'Get your hand in,' says Nanny.

We are half-way up the hill.

And then I see, after all, some trees have gone down. Tree-tops lower than her waist.

And my Nanny is walking on the rim of the world.

This is family history: She had six of us grandchildren. Sh———
me up the hill to see my newborn baby sister.

In the memory, she is taller than trees.

She is big, her jaws wobble. Her hands are round the handle. Crackle-crackle in the wheels.

'Get your hand in,' she says, 'you are big enough to know better.'

I am big. She is biggest.

But I am bigger than I was.

Now there is somebody smaller than me.

We go under the trees.

Dark splotches dive into the pram and swoop up out again.

The hill is steeper. She bends over to push and her wobbling jaws come down to join her hands.

'You are a weight,' she says. She is puffing. 'Your weight is something.'

I am heavy. I am bigger. But I need to be pushed. She can push. The brown bits swish. Dark splotches swim across her face and hands.

Where do they come from?

'From the trees.' The brown bits are down, and dark smudges are flying, coming off the trees.

Down below and behind, is a bright green hole, filled with tree-top cushions. My Nanny's heels are kicking the tops of the trees.

The pram was old. She had used it previously for her own children.

We come out into the sun again. The black smudges shoot off. The pram-sides light up, dusty blue. Nanny's dark dress fades. The cloth glimmers as she moves. The sun burns my legs. In the wheel a dry bit crackles.

Now her hands on the pram are stretched and shining.

They have faint brown blotches.

Look, the shadows have left marks.

'Oh, aye,' says Nanny, 'they're the marks of growing old.'

We have come through the trees.

She is older.

I am bigger.

She clenches tight, pushing the pram to the peak of the world.

She wasn't young when she married. Her husband was younger, the quiet, shamefaced son of a drunkard. She bore him four children. She pushed her children round in the big blue pram.

More brown bits get caught. Tack-tack.

I lean over to see.

'Don't lean over,' says Nanny.

We reach the top. She stops the pram. She straightens up to get her breath. Her face floats up away from her hands. Something winks on her front. Brooch. She keeps it in a box at the side of the bed. Her bed. And Grandpa's. Grandpa throws me up: God, you're a weight.

My weight is something.

We are tall, and resting on the peak of the world.

He wasn't like most men. Teetotal, industrious. And good with the children. She loved that husband.

She looks down and round at the dry bits in the wheel. She stoops, her head drops below the side of the pram. She keeps hold with one hand. One hand on the handle. I lean over to watch. Her hair is parted and caught in a brown thing. Comb. She keeps it with the brooch. Along the parting I can see the skin of her head has the shadowy blotch-marks. One mottled hand and her head jerk below the pram-side. The pram rocks, I hold the sides.

'Don't lean over,' she says, 'you'll tip. Your weight is something.'

I am something.

I am bigger. I am bigger than the baby.

I wait, high in my pram, while she clears the wheels on the rim of the world.

Few could have hoped to make such a blessed marriage. Her daughters could hardly expect to be so lucky. Yet they loved their men.

She stands. She is puffing.

She says, 'We'd better get on. Your Mam will be sending your Dad out to find us.'

My Daddy throws me, up towards the ceiling, and then I am falling . . .

My Nanny's hands go up behind her head. She pushes the comb in. Her stomach bulges round the handle.

The pram jerks, and then she is running. Everything slips; something sweet and sharp is pulling in my tummy. Her hair flies out from her forehead, all the wispy bits escaping.

Her comb slips out and is gone, a brown bit fallen down the side of the world.

She had four children. Three survived.

Next in the memory, her hand is on the door. She hol' her. I am tucked beneath her bulges. She smells sweet blotchy hand pushes the wood and makes an opening. My mummy's voice curls through it.

'Come on in, come on, where are you?'

In the room it is dim. My Mummy sits in the bed. Her knees are up, like a mountain.

There is something on her face.

She says, 'Here's your baby sister.'

What is that that's on her face?

My Nanny steers me over. She says, 'See, your baby sister!'

Along my Mummy's cheek is a big brown blotch-thing. She smiles, the brown thing twitches.

She says, 'It's just a little burn.'

My Mummy looks at my Nanny. She says, 'It's the ether; the mask slipped.'

My Nanny lifts me past the mountain: 'See, there's your baby sister.'

My Nanny nods at my Mummy.

She had four childbirths of her own. The fourth was a stillbirth.

That is all; after all there are no men in the memory. Just my Mummy's face with its stark burnt leaf; the dark flake of the baby lying over the mountain, over the edge of the world beside her; and my Nanny, her shadowed hands in her lap, folded and fallen.

J. G. Ballard

Memories of the Space Age

J. G. Ballard was born in 1930 in Shanghai, where his father was a businessman. After the attack on Pearl Harbor, Ballard and his family were placed in a civilian prison camp. They returned to England in 1946. After two years at Cambridge, where he read medicine, Ballard worked as a copywriter and Covent Garden porter before going to Canada with the RAF. In 1956 his first short story was published in *New Worlds* and he took a full-time job on a technical journal, moving on to become assistant editor of a scientific journal, where he stayed until 1961. His first novel, *The Drowned World*, was written in the same year. His other books include: *The Four-Dimensional Nightmare* (1963), *The Terminal Beach* (1964), *The Atrocity Exhibition* (1970), *Crash* (1973), *Concrete Island* (1974), *High-Rise* (1975), *The Unlimited Dream Company* (1979) and *Myths of the Near Future* (1982).

All day this strange pilot had flown his antique aeroplane over the abandoned space centre, a frantic machine lost in the silence of Florida. The flapping engine of the old Curtiss biplane woke Dr Mallory soon after dawn, as he lay asleep beside his exhausted wife on the fifth floor of the empty hotel in Titusville. Dreams of the space age had filled the night, memories of white runways as calm as glaciers, now broken by this eccentric aircraft veering around like the fragment of a disturbed mind.

From his balcony Mallory watched the ancient biplane circle the rusty gantries of Cape Kennedy. The sunlight flared against the pilot's helmet, illuminating the cat's cradle of silver wires that pinioned the open fuselage between the wings, a puzzle from which the pilot was trying to escape by a series of loops and rolls. Ignoring him, the plane flew back and forth above the forest canopy, its engine calling across the immense deserted decks, as if this ghost of the pioneer days of aviation could summon the sleeping titans of the Apollo programme from their graves beneath the cracked concrete.

Giving up for the moment, the Curtiss turned from the gantries and set course inland for Titusville. As it clattered over the hotel Mallory recognized the familiar hard stare behind the pilot's goggles. Each morning the same pilot appeared, flying a succession of antique craft – relics, Mallory assumed, from some forgotten museum at a private airfield nearby. There were a Spad and a Sopwith Camel, a replica of the Wright Flyer, and a Fokker triplane that had buzzed the NASA causeway the previous day, driving inland thousands of frantic gulls and swallows, denying them any share of the sky.

Standing naked on the balcony, Mallory let the amber air warm his skin. He counted the ribs below his shoulder blades, aware that for the first time he could feel his kidneys. Despite the hours spent foraging each day, and the canned food looted from the abandoned supermarkets, it was difficult to keep up his body weight. In the two months since they set out from Vancouver on the slow, nervous drive back to Florida, he and Anne had each lost more than thirty pounds, as if their bodies were carrying out a reinventory of themselves for the coming world without time. But the bones endured. His skeleton seemed to grow stronger and heavier, preparing itself for the unnourished sleep of the grave.

Already sweating in the humid air, Mallory returned to the bedroom. Anne had woken, but lay motionless in the centre of the bed, strands of blond hair caught like a child's in her mouth. With its fixed and empty expression, her face resembled a clock that had just stopped. Mallory sat down and placed his hands on her diaphragm, gently respiring her. Every morning he feared that time would run out for Anne while she slept, leaving her for ever in the middle of a nightmare.

She stared at Mallory, as if surprised to wake in this shabby resort hotel with a man she had possibly known for years but for some reason failed to recognize.

'Hinton?'

'Not yet.' Mallory steered the hair from her mouth. 'Do I look like him now?'

'God, I'm going blind.' Anne wiped her nose on the pillow. She raised her wrists, and stared at the two watches that formed a pair of time-cuffs. The stores in Florida were filled with clocks and watches that had been left behind in case they might be contaminated, and each day Anne selected a new set of timepieces. She touched Mallory reassuringly. 'All men look the same, Edward. That's streetwalker's wisdom for you. But I meant the plane.'

'I'm not sure. It wasn't a spotter aircraft. Clearly the police don't bother to come to Cape Kennedy any more.'

'I don't blame them. It's an evil place. Edward, we ought to leave, let's get out this morning.'

Mallory held her shoulders, trying to calm this frayed but still handsome woman. He needed her to look her best for Hinton. 'Anne, we've only been here a week – let's give it a little more time.'

'Time? Edward ...' She took Mallory's hands in a sudden show of affection. 'Dear, that's one thing we've run out of. I'm getting those headaches again, just like the ones I had fifteen years ago. It's uncanny, I can feel the same nerves ...'

'I'll give you something, you can sleep this afternoon.'

'No ... They're a warning. I want to feel every twinge.' She pressed the wrist-watches to her temples, as if trying to tune her brain to their signal. 'We were mad to come here, and even more mad to stay for a second longer than we need.'

'I know. It's a long shot but worth a try. I've learned one thing in all these years – if there's a way out, we'll find it at Cape Kennedy.'

'We won't! Everything's poisoned here. We should go to Australia, like all the other NASA people.' Anne rooted in her handbag on the floor, heaving aside an illustrated encyclopaedia of birds she had found in a Titusville bookstore. 'I looked it up – western Australia is as far from Florida as you can go. It's almost the exact antipodes. Edward, my sister lives in *Perth*. I knew there was a reason why she invited us there.'

Mallory stared at the distant gantries of Cape Kennedy. It was difficult to believe that he had once worked there. 'I don't think even Perth, Australia, is far enough. We need to set out into space again ...'

Anne shuddered. 'Edward, don't say that – a *crime* was committed here, everyone knows that's how it all began.' As they listened to the distant drone of the aircraft she gazed at her broad hips and soft thighs. Equal to the challenge, her chin lifted. 'Noisy, isn't it? Do you think Hinton is here? He may not remember me.'

'He'll remember you. You were the only one who liked him.'

'Well, in a sort of way. How long was he in prison before he escaped? Twenty years?'

'A long time. Perhaps he'll take you flying again. You enjoyed that.'

'Yes ... He was strange. But even if he is here, can he help? He was the one who started it all.'

'No, not Hinton.' Mallory listened to his voice in the empty hotel. It seemed deeper and more resonant, as the slowing time stretched out the frequencies. 'In point of fact, I started it all.'

Anne had turned from him and lay on her side, a watch pressed to each ear. Mallory reminded himself to go out and begin his morning search for food. Food, a vitamin shot, and a clean pair of sheets. Sex with Anne, which he had hoped would keep them bickering and awake, had generated affection instead. Suppose they conceived a child, here at Cape Kennedy, within the shadow of the gantries ... ?

He remembered the mongol and autistic children he had left behind at the clinic in Vancouver, and his firm belief – strongly contested by his fellow physicians and the worn-out parents – that these were diseases of time, malfunctions of the temporal sense that marooned these children on small islands of awareness, a few minutes in the case of the mongols, a span of micro-seconds for the autistics. A child conceived and born here at Cape Kennedy would be born into a world without time, an indefinite and unending present, that primeval paradise that the old brain remembered so vividly, seen both by those living for the first time and by those dying for the first time. It was curious that images of heaven or paradise always presented a static world, not the kinetic eternity one would expect, the roller-coaster of a hyperactive funfair, the screaming Luna Parks of LSD and psilocybin. It was a strange paradox that given eternity, an infinity of time, they chose to eliminate the very element offered in such abundance.

Still, if they stayed much longer at Cape Kennedy he and Anne would soon return to the world of the old brain, like those first tragic astronauts he had helped to put into space. During the previous year in Vancouver there had been too many attacks, those periods of largo when time seemed to slow, an afternoon at his desk stretched into days. His own lapses in concentration both he and his colleagues put down to eccentricity, but Anne's growing vagueness had been impossible to ignore, the first clear signs of the space sickness that began to slow the clock, as it had done first for the astronauts and then for all the other NASA personnel based in Florida. Within the last months the attacks had come five or six times a day, periods when everything began to slow down, he would apparently spend all day shaving or signing a cheque.

Time, like a film reel running through a faulty projector, was moving at an erratic pace, at moments backing up and almost coming to a halt, then speeding on again. One day soon it would stop, freeze forever on one frame. Had it really taken them two months to drive from Vancouver, weeks alone from Jacksonville to Cape Kennedy?

He thought of the long journey down the Florida coast, a world of immense empty hotels and glutinous time, of strange meetings with Anne in deserted corridors, of sex-acts that seemed to last for days. Now and then, in forgotten bedrooms, they came across other couples who had strayed into Florida, into the eternal present of this timeless zone, Paolo and Francesca forever embracing in the Fontainebleau Hotel. In some of those eyes there had been horror ...

As for Anne and himself, time had run out of their marriage fifteen years ago, driven away by the spectres of the space complex, and by memories of Hinton. They had come back here like Adam and Eve returning to the Edenic paradise with an unfortunate dose of VD. Thankfully, as time evaporated, so did memory. He looked at his few possessions, now almost meaningless – the tape machine on which he recorded his steady decline; an album of nude Polaroid poses of a woman doctor he had known in Vancouver; his Gray's *Anatomy* from his student days, a unique work of fiction, pages still stained with formalin from the dissecting-room cadavers; a paperback selection of Muybridge's stop-frame photographs; and a psychoanalytic study of Simon Magus.

'Anne ...?' The light in the bedroom had become brighter, there was a curious glare, like the white runways of his dreams. Nothing moved, for a moment Mallory felt that they were waxworks in a museum tableau, or in a painting by Edward Hopper of a tired couple in a provincial hotel. The dream-time was creeping up on him, about to enfold him. As always he felt no fear, his pulse was calmer ...

There was a blare of noise outside, a shadow flashed across the balcony. The Curtiss biplane roared overhead, then sped low across the rooftops of Titusville. Roused by the sudden movement, Mallory stood up and shook himself, slapping his thighs to spur on his heart. The plane had caught him just in time.

'Anne, I think that was Hinton ...'

She lay on her side, the watches to her ears. Mallory stroked her cheeks, but her eyes rolled away from him. She breathed peacefully with her upper lungs, her pulse as slow as a hibernating mammal's. He drew the sheet across her shoulders. She would wake in an hour's time, with a vivid memory of a single image, a rehearsal for those last seconds before time finally froze ...

2

Medical case in hand, Mallory stepped into the street through the broken plate-glass window of the supermarket. The abandoned store had become his chief source of supplies. Tall palms split the sidewalks in front of the boarded-up shops and bars, providing a shaded promenade through the empty town. Several times he had been caught out in the open during an attack, but the palms had shielded his skin from the Florida sun. For a reason he had yet to understand, he liked to walk naked through the silent streets, watched by the orioles and parakeets. The naked doctor, physician to the birds ... perhaps they would pay him in feathers, the midnight-blue tail-plumes of the macaws, the golden wings of the orioles, sufficient fees for him to build a flying machine of his own?

The medical case was heavy, loaded with packet rice, sugar, cartons of pasta. He would light a small fire on another balcony and cook up a starchy meal, carefully boiling the brackish water in the roof tank. Mallory paused in the hotel car-park, gathering his strength for the climb to the fifth floor, above the rat and cockroach line. He rested in the front seat of the police patrol car they had commandeered in a deserted suburb of Jacksonville. Anne had regretted leaving behind her classy Toyota, but the exchange had been sensible. Not only would the unexpected sight of this squad car confuse any military spotter planes, but the hotted-up Dodge could outrun most light aircraft.

Mallory was relying on the car's power to trap the mysterious pilot who appeared each morning in his antique aeroplanes. He had noticed that as every day passed these veteran machines tended to be of increasingly older vintage. Sooner or later the pilot would find himself well within Mallory's reach, unable to shake off the pursuing Dodge before being forced to land at his secret airfield.

Mallory listened to the police radio, the tuneless static that reflected the huge void that lay over Florida. By contrast the air-traffic frequencies were a babel of intercom chatter, both from the big jets landing at Mobile, Atlanta and Savannah, and from military craft overflying the Bahamas. All gave Florida a wide berth. To the north of the 31st parallel life in the United States went on as before, but south of that unfenced and rarely patrolled frontier was an immense silence of deserted marinas and shopping malls, abandoned citrus farms and retirement estates, silent ghettoes and airports.

Losing interest in Mallory, the birds were rising into the air. A dappled shadow crossed the car-park, and Mallory looked up as a graceful, slender-winged aircraft drifted lazily past the roof of the hotel. Its twin-bladed propeller struck the air like a child's paddle, driven at a leisurely pace by the pilot sitting astride the bicycle pedals within the transparent fuselage. A man-powered glider of advanced design, it soared silently above the rooftops, buoyed by the thermals rising from the empty town.

'Hinton!' Certain now that he could catch the former astronaut, Mallory abandoned his groceries and pulled himself behind the wheel of the police car. By the time he started the flooded engine he had lost sight of the glider. Its delicate wings, almost as long as an airliner's, had drifted across the forest canopy, kept company by the flocks of swallows and martins that rose to inspect this timorous intruder of their air-space. Mallory reversed out of the car-park and set off after the glider, veering in and out of the palms that lifted from the centre of the street.

Calming himself, he scanned the side roads, and caught sight of

the machine circling the jai alai stadium on the southern outskirts
of the town. A cloud of gulls surrounded the glider, some mobbing
its lazy propeller, others taking up their station above its wing-tips.
The pilot seemed to be urging them to follow him, enticing them with
gentle rolls and yaws, drawing them back towards the sea and to the
forest causeways of the space complex.

Reducing his speed, Mallory followed three hundred yards behind
the glider. They crossed the bridge over the Banana River, heading
towards the NASA causeway and the derelict bars and motels of Cocoa
Beach. The nearest of the gantries was still over a mile away to the
north, but Mallory was aware that he had entered the outer zone
of the space grounds. A threatening aura emanated from these ancient
towers, as old in their way as the great temple columns of Karnak,
bearers of a different cosmic order, symbols of a view of the universe
that had been abandoned along with the state of Florida that had
given them birth.

Looking down at the now clear waters of the Banana River, Mallory
found himself avoiding the sombre forests that packed the causeways
and concrete decks of the space complex, smothering the signs and
fences, the camera towers and observation bunkers. Time was different
here, as it had been at Alamagordo and Eniwetok, a psychic fissure
had riven both time and space, then run deep into the minds of the
people who worked here. Through that new suture in his skull time
leaked into the slack water below the car. The forest oaks were waiting
for him to feed their roots, these motionless trees were as insane as
anything in the visions of Max Ernst. There were the same insatiable
birds, feeding on the vegetation that sprang from the corpses of trapped
aircraft . . .

Above the causeway the gulls were wheeling in alarm, screaming
against the sky. The powered glider side-slipped out of the air, circled
and soared along the bridge, its miniature undercarriage only ten feet
above the police car. The pilot pedalled rapidly, propeller flashing
at the alarmed sun, and Mallory caught a glimpse of blond hair and
a woman's face in the transparent cockpit. A red silk scarf flew from
her throat.

'Hinton!' As Mallory shouted into the noisy air the pilot leaned
from the cockpit and pointed to a slip road running through the
forest towards Cocoa Beach, then banked behind the trees and
vanished.

Hinton? For some bizarre reason the former astronaut was now masquerading as a woman in a blond wig, luring him back to the space complex. The birds had been in league with him . . .

The sky was empty, the gulls had vanished across the river into the forest. Mallory stopped the car. He was about to step on to the road when he heard the drone of an aero-engine. The Fokker triplane had emerged from the space centre. It made a tight circuit of the gantries and came in across the sea. Fifty feet above the beach, it swept across the palmettos and saw-grass, its twin machine-guns pointing straight towards the police car.

Mallory began to re-start the engine, when the machine-guns above the pilot's windshield opened fire at him. He assumed that the pilot was shooting blank ammunition left over from some air display. Then the first bullets struck the metalled road a hundred feet ahead. The second burst threw the car on to its flattened front tyres, severed the door pillar by the passenger seat and filled the cabin with exploding glass. As the plane climbed steeply, about to make its second pass at him, Mallory brushed the blood-flecked glass from his chest and thighs. He leapt from the car and vaulted over the metal railing into the shallow culvert beside the bridge, as his blood ran away through the water towards the waiting forest of the space grounds.

3

From the shelter of the culvert, Mallory watched the police car burning on the bridge. The column of oily smoke rose a thousand feet into the empty sky, a beacon visible for ten miles around the Cape. The flocks of gulls had vanished. The powered glider and its woman pilot – he remembered her warning him of the Fokker's approach – had slipped away to its lair somewhere south along the coast.

Too stunned to rest, Mallory stared at the mile-long causeway. It would take him half an hour to walk back to the mainland, an easy target for Hinton as he waited in the Fokker above the clouds. Had the former astronaut recognized Mallory and immediately guessed why the sometime NASA physician had come to search for him?

Too exhausted to swim the Banana River, Mallory waded ashore and set off through the trees. He decided to spend the afternoon in one of the abandoned motels in Cocoa Beach, then make his way back to Titusville after dark.

The forest floor was cool against his bare feet, but a soft light fell through the leafy canopy and warmed his skin. Already the blood had dried on his chest and shoulders, a vivid tracery like an aboriginal tattoo that seemed more suitable wear for this violent and uncertain realm than the clothes he had left behind at the hotel. He passed the rusting hulk of an Airstream trailer, its steel capsule overgrown with lianas and ground ivy, as if the trees had reached up to seize a passing space craft and dragged it down into the undergrowth. There were abandoned cars and the remains of camping equipment, moss-covered chairs and tables around old barbecue spits left here twenty years earlier when the sightseers had hurriedly vacated the state.

Mallory stepped through this terminal moraine, the elements of a forgotten theme park arranged by a demolition squad. Already he felt that he belonged to an older world within the forest, a realm of darkness, patience and unseen life. The beach was a hundred yards away, the Atlantic breakers washing the empty sand. A school of dolphins leapt cleanly through the water, on their way south to the Gulf. The birds had gone, but the fish were ready to take their place in the air.

Mallory welcomed them. He knew that he had been walking down this sand-bar for little more than half an hour, but at the same time he felt that he had been there for days, even possibly weeks and months. In part of his mind he had always been there. The minutes were beginning to stretch, urged on by this eventless universe free of birds and aircraft. His memory faltered, he was forgetting his past, the clinic at Vancouver and its wounded children, his wife asleep in the hotel at Titusville, even his own identity. A single moment was a small instalment of forever – he plucked a fern leaf and watched it for minutes as it fell slowly to the ground, deferring to gravity in the most elegant way.

Aware now that he was entering the dream-time, Mallory ran on through the trees. He was moving in slow-motion, his weak legs carrying him across the leafy ground with the grace of an Olympic athlete. He raised his hand to touch a butterfly apparently asleep on the wing, embarking his outstretched fingers on an endless journey.

The forest that covered the sand-bar began to thin out, giving way to the beach-houses and motels of Cocoa Beach. A derelict hotel sat among the trees, its gates collapsed across the drive, Spanish moss hanging from a sign that advertised a zoo and theme park devoted to the space age. Through the waist-high palmettos the chromium and neon rockets rose from their stands like figures on amusement park carousels.

Laughing to himself, Mallory vaulted the gates and ran on past the rusting space ships. Behind the theme park were overgrown tennis courts, a swimming pool and the remains of the small zoo, with an alligator pit, mammal cages and aviary. Happily, Mallory saw that the tenants had returned to their homes. An overweight zebra dozed in his concrete enclosure, a bored tiger stared in a cross-eyed way at his own nose, and an elderly caiman sunbathed on the grass beside the alligator pit.

Time was slowing now, coming almost to a halt. Mallory hung in mid-step, his bare feet in the air above the ground. Parked on the tiled path beside the swimming pool was a huge transparent dragonfly, the powered glider he had chased that morning.

Two wizened cheetahs sat in the shade under its wing, watching Mallory with their prim eyes. One of them rose from the ground and slowly launched itself towards him, but it was twenty feet away and Mallory knew that it would never reach him. Its threadbare coat, re-fashioned from some old carpet bag, stretched itself into a lazy arch that seemed to freeze forever in mid-frame.

Mallory waited for time to stop. The waves were no longer running towards the beach, and were frozen ruffs of icing sugar. Fish hung in the sky, the wise dolphins happy to be in their new realm, faces smiling in the sun. The water spraying from the fountain at the shallow end of the pool now formed a glass parasol.

Only the cheetah was moving, still able to outrun time. It was now ten feet from him, its head tilted to one side as it aimed itself at Mallory's throat, its yellow claws more pointed than Hinton's bullets. But Mallory felt no fear for this violent cat. Without time it could never reach him, without time the lion could at last lie down with the lamb, the eagle with the vole.

He looked up at the vivid light, noticing the figure of a young woman who hung in the air with outstretched arms above the diving board. Suspended over the water in a swallow dive, her naked body flew as serenely as the dolphins above the sea. Her calm face gazed at the glass floor ten feet below her small, extended palms. She seemed un-aware of Mallory, her eyes fixed on the mystery of her own flight, and he could see clearly the red marks left on her shoulders by the harness straps of the glider, and the silver arrow of her appendix scar pointing to her child-like pubis.

The cheetah was closer now, its claws picking at the threads of dried blood that laced Mallory's shoulders, its grey muzzle retracted to show its ulcerated gums and stained teeth. If he reached out he could embrace it, comfort all the memories of Africa, soothe the violence from its old pelt ...

4

Time had flowed out of Florida, as it had from the space age. After a brief pause, like a trapped film reel running free, it sped on again, rekindling a kinetic world.

Mallory sat in a deck chair beside the pool, watching the cheetahs as they rested in the shade under the glider. They crossed and uncrossed their paws like card-dealers palming an ace, now and then lifting their noses at the scent of this strange man and his blood.

Despite their sharp teeth, Mallory felt calm and rested, a sleeper waking from a complex but satisfying dream. He was glad to be surrounded by this little zoo with its backdrop of playful rockets, as innocent as an illustration from a children's book.

The young woman stood next to Mallory, keeping a concerned watch on him. She had dressed while Mallory recovered from his collision with the cheetah. After dragging away the boisterous beast she settled Mallory in the deck chair, then pulled on a patched leather flying suit. Was this the only clothing she had ever worn? A true child of the air, born and sleeping on the wing. With her over-bright mascara and blond hair brushed into a vivid peruke, she resembled a leather-garbed parakeet, a punk madonna of the airways. Worn NASA flashes on her shoulder gave her a biker's swagger. On the name-plate above her right breast was printed: *Nightingale*.

'Poor man – are you back? You're far, far away.' Behind the child-like features, the soft mouth and boneless nose, a pair of adult eyes watched him warily. 'Hey, you – what happened to your uniform? Are you in the police?'

Mallory took her hand, touching the heavy Apollo signet ring she wore on her wedding finger. From somewhere came the absurd notion that she was married to Hinton. Then he noticed her enlarged pupils, a hint of fever.

'Don't worry – I'm a doctor, Edward Mallory. I'm on holiday here with my wife.'

'Holiday?' The girl shook her head, relieved but baffled. 'That patrol car – I thought someone had stolen your uniform while you were ... out. Dear doctor, no one comes on holiday to Florida any more. If you don't leave soon this is one vacation that may last forever.'

'I know ...' Mallory looked round at the zoo with its dozing tiger, the gay fountain and cheerful rockets. This was the amiable world of the Douanier Rousseau's *Merry Jesters*. He accepted the jeans and shirt which the girl gave him. He had liked being naked, not from any exhibitionist urge, but because it suited the vanished realm he had just visited. The impassive tiger with his skin of fire belonged to that world of light. 'Perhaps I've come to the right place, though – I'd like to spend forever here. To tell the truth, I've just had a small taste of what forever is going to be like.'

'No, thanks.' Intrigued by Mallory, the girl squatted on the grass beside him. 'Tell me, how often are you getting the attacks?'

'Every day. Probably more than I realize. And you ... ?' When she shook her head a little too quickly, Mallory added: 'They're not that frightening, you know. In a way you want to go back.'

'I can see. Doctor, you ought to be worried by that. Take your wife and leave – any moment now all the clocks are going to stop.'

'That's why we're here – it's our one chance. My wife has even less time left than I have. We want to come to terms with everything – whatever that means. Not much any more.'

'Doctor ... The real Cape Kennedy is inside your head, not out here.' Clearly unsettled by the presence of this marooned physician, the girl pulled on her flying helmet. She scanned the sky, where the gulls and swallows were again gathering, drawn into the air by the distant drone of an aero-engine. 'Listen – an hour ago you were nearly killed. I tried to warn you. Our local stunt pilot doesn't like the police.'

'So I found out. I'm glad he didn't hit you. I thought he was flying your glider.'

'Hinton? He wouldn't be seen dead in that. He needs speed. Hinton's trying to join the birds.'

'Hinton ...' Repeating the name, Mallory felt a surge of fear and relief, realizing that he was committed now to the course of action he had planned months ago when he left the clinic in Vancouver. 'So Hinton is here.'

'He's here.' The girl nodded at Mallory, still unsure that he was not a policeman. 'Not many people remember Hinton.'

'I remember Hinton.' As she fingered the Apollo signet ring he asked: 'You're not married to him?'

'To Hinton? Doctor, you have some strange ideas. What are your patients like?'

'I often wonder. But you know Hinton?'

'Who does? He has other things in his mind. He fixed the pool here, and brought me the glider from the museum at Orlando.' She added, archly: 'Disneyland East – that's what they called Cape Kennedy in the early days.'

'I remember – twenty years ago I worked for NASA.'

'So did my father.' She spoke sharply, angered by the mention of the space agency. 'He was the last astronaut – Alan Shepley – the only one who didn't come back. And the only one they didn't wait for.'

'Shepley was *your* father?' Startled, Mallory turned to look at the distant gantries of the launching grounds. 'He died in the Shuttle. Then you know that Hinton . . .'

'Doctor, I don't think it was Hinton who really killed my father.' Before Mallory could speak she lowered her goggles over her eyes. 'Anyway, it doesn't matter now. The important thing is that someone will be here when he comes down.'

'You're waiting for him?'

'Shouldn't I, doctor?'

'Yes . . . but it was a long time ago. Besides, it's a million to one against him coming down here.'

'That's not true. According to Hinton, Dad may actually come down somewhere along this coast. Hinton says the orbits are starting to decay. I search the beaches every day.'

Mallory smiled at her encouragingly, admiring this spunky but sad child. He remembered the news photographs of the astronaut's daughter, Gale Shepley, a babe in arms fiercely cradled by the widow outside the courtroom after the verdict. 'I hope he comes. And your little zoo, Gale?'

'Nightingale,' she corrected. 'The zoo is for Dad. I want the world to be a special place for us when we go.'

'You're leaving together?'

'In a sense – like you, doctor, and everyone else here.'

'So you do get the attacks.'

'Not often – that's why I keep moving. The birds are teaching me how to fly. Did you know that, doctor? The birds are trying to get out of time.'

Already she was distracted by the unswept sky and the massing birds. After tying up the cheetahs she made her way quickly to the glider. 'I have to leave, doctor. Can you ride a motorcycle? There's a Yamaha in the hotel lobby you can borrow.'

But before taking off she confided to Mallory: 'It's all wishful thinking, doctor, for Hinton too. When Dad comes it won't matter any more.'

*

Mallory tried to help her launch the glider, but the filmy craft took off within its own length. Pedalling swiftly, she propelled it into the air, climbing over the chromium rockets of the theme park. The glider circled the hotel, then levelled its long, tapering wings and set off for the empty beaches of the north.

Restless without her, the tiger began to wrestle with the truck tyre suspended from the ceiling of its cage. For a moment Mallory was tempted to unlock the door and join it. Avoiding the cheetahs chained to the diving board, he entered the empty hotel and took the staircase to the roof. From the ladder of the elevator house he watched the glider moving towards the space centre.

Alan Shepley – the first man to be murdered in space. All too well Mallory remembered the young pilot of the Shuttle, one of the last astronauts to be launched from Cape Kennedy before the curtain came down on the space age. A former Apollo pilot, Shepley had been a dedicated but likeable young man, as ambitious as the other astronauts and yet curiously naïve.

Mallory, like everyone else, had much preferred him to the Shuttle's co-pilot, a research physicist who was then the token civilian among the astronauts. Mallory remembered how he had instinctively disliked Hinton on their first meeting at the medical centre. But from the start he had been fascinated by the man's awkwardness and irritability. In its closing days, the space programme had begun to attract people who were slightly unbalanced, and he recognized that Hinton belonged to this second generation of astronauts, mavericks with complex motives of their own, quite unlike the disciplined service pilots who had furnished the Mercury and Apollo flight-crews. Hinton had the intense and obsessive temperament of a Cortez, Pizarro or Drake, the hot blood and cold heart. It was Hinton who had exposed for the first time so many of the latent conundrums at the heart of the space programme, those psychological dimensions that had been ignored from its start and subsequently revealed, too late, in the crack-ups of the early astronauts, their slides into mysticism and melancholia.

'The best astronauts never dream,' Russell Schweickart had once remarked. Not only did Hinton dream, he had torn the whole fabric of time and space, cracked the hour-glass from which time was running. Mallory was aware of his own complicity, he had been chiefly responsible for putting Shepley and Hinton together, guessing that the repressed and earnest Shepley might provide the trigger for a metaphysical experiment of a special sort.

At all events, Shepley's death had been the first murder in space, a crisis that Mallory had both stage-managed and unconsciously welcomed. The murder of the astronaut and the public unease that followed had marked the end of the space age, an awareness that man had committed an evolutionary crime by travelling into space, that he was tampering with the elements of his own consciousness. The fracture of that fragile continuum erected by the human psyche through millions of years had soon shown itself, in the confused sense of time displayed by the astronauts and NASA personnel, and then by the inhabitants of the towns near the space centre. Cape Kennedy and the whole of Florida itself became a poisoned land to be for ever avoided like the nuclear testing grounds of Nevada and Utah.

Yet, perhaps, instead of going mad in space, Hinton had been the first man to 'go sane'. During his trial he pleaded his innocence and then refused to defend himself, viewing the international media circus with a stoicism that at times seemed bizarre. That silence had un-nerved everyone – how could Hinton believe himself innocent of a murder (he had locked Shepley into the docking module, vented his air supply and then cast him loose in his coffin, keeping up a matter-of-fact commentary the whole while) committed in full view of a thousand million television witnesses?

Alcatraz had been re-commissioned for Hinton, for this solitary prisoner isolated on the frigid island to prevent him contaminating the rest of the human race. After twenty years he was safely forgotten, and even the report of his escape was only briefly mentioned. He was presumed to have died, after crashing into the icy waters of the bay in a small aircraft he had secretly constructed. Mallory had travelled down to San Francisco to see the waterlogged craft, a curious ornithopter built from the yew trees that Hinton had been allowed to grow in the prison island's stony soil, boosted by a home-made rocket engine powered by a fertilizer-based explosive. He had waited twenty years for the slow-growing evergreens to be strong enough to form the wings that would carry him to freedom.

Then, only six months after Hinton's death, Mallory had been told by an old NASA colleague of the strange stunt pilot who had been seen flying his antique aircraft at Cape Kennedy, some native of the air who had so far eluded the half-hearted attempts to ground him. The descriptions of the bird-cage aeroplanes reminded Mallory of the drowned ornithopter dragged up on to the winter beach ...

So Hinton had returned to Cape Kennedy. As Mallory set off on the Yamaha along the coast road, past the deserted motels and cock-tail bars of Cocoa Beach, he looked out at the bright Atlantic sand, so unlike the rocky shingle of the prison island. But was the ornithopter a decoy, like all the antique aircraft that Hinton flew above the space centre, machines that concealed some other aim?

Some other escape?

5

Fifteen minutes later, as Mallory sped along the NASA causeway towards Titusville, he was overtaken by an old Wright biplane. Crossing the Banana River, he noticed that the noise of a second engine had drowned the Yamaha's. The venerable flying machine appeared above the trees, the familiar gaunt-faced pilot sitting in the open cockpit. Barely managing to pull ahead of the Yamaha, the pilot flew down to within ten feet of the road, gesturing to Mallory to stop, then cut back his engine and settled the craft on to the weed-grown concrete.

'Mallory, I've been looking for you! Come on, doctor!'

Mallory hesitated, the gritty backwash of the Wright's props stinging the open wounds under his shirt. As he peered among the struts Hinton seized his arm and lifted him on to the passenger seat.

'Mallory, yes ... it's you still!' Hinton pushed his goggles back on to his bony forehead, revealing a pair of blood-flecked eyes. He gazed at Mallory with open amazement, as if surprised that Mallory had aged at all in the past twenty years, but delighted that he had somehow survived. 'Nightingale just told me you were here. Doctor Mysterium ... I nearly killed you!'

'You're trying again ...!' Mallory clung to the frayed seat straps as Hinton opened the throttle. The biplane gazelled into the air. In a gust of wind across the exposed causeway it flew backwards for a few seconds, then climbed vertically and banked across the trees towards the distant gantries. Thousands of swallows and martins overtook them on all sides, ignoring Hinton as if well-used to this erratic aviator and his absurd machines.

As Hinton worked the rudder tiller, Mallory glanced at this feverish and undernourished man. The years in prison and the rushing air above Cape Kennedy had leached all trace of iron salts from his pallid skin. His raw eyelids, the nail-picked septum of his strong nose and his scarred lips were blanched almost silver in the wind. He had gone beyond exhaustion and malnutrition into a nervous realm where the rival elements of his warring mind were locked together like the cogs of an overwound clock. As he pummelled Mallory's arm it was clear that he had already forgotten the years since their last meeting. He pointed to the forest below them, to the viaducts, concrete decks and blockhouses, eager to show off his domain.

They had reached the heart of the space complex, where the gantries rose like gallows put out to rent. In the centre was the giant crawler, the last of the Shuttles mounted vertically on its launching platform. Its rusting tracks lay around it, the chains of an unshackled colossus.

Here at Cape Kennedy time had not stood still but moved into reverse. The huge fuel tank and auxiliary motors of the Shuttle resembled the domes and minarets of a replica Taj Mahal. Lines of antique aircraft were drawn up on the runway below the crawler – a Lilienthal glider lying on its side like an ornate fan window, a Mignet Flying Flea, the Fokker, Spad and Sopwith Camel, and a Wright Flyer that went back to the earliest days of aviation. As they circled the launch platform Mallory almost expected to see a crowd of Edwardian aviators thronging this display of ancient craft, pilots in gaiters and overcoats, women passengers in hats fitted with leather straps.

Other ghosts haunted the daylight at Cape Kennedy. When they landed Mallory stepped into the shadow of the launch platform, an iron cathedral shunned by the sky. An unsettling silence came in from the dense forest that filled the once open decks of the space centre, from the eyeless bunkers and rusting camera towers.

'Mallory, I'm glad you came!' Hinton pulled off his flying helmet, exposing a lumpy scalp under his close-cropped hair – Mallory remembered that he had once been attacked by a berserk warder. 'I couldn't believe it was you! And Anne? Is she all right?'

'She's here, at the hotel in Titusville.'

'I know, I've just seen her on the roof. She looked ...' Hinton's voice dropped, in his concern he had forgotten what he was doing. He began to walk in a circle, and then rallied himself. 'Still, it's good to see you. It's more than I hoped for – you were the one person who knew what was going on here.'

'Did I?' Mallory searched for the sun, hidden behind the cold bulk of the launch platform. Cape Kennedy was even more sinister than he had expected, like some ancient death camp. 'I don't think I –'

'Of course you knew! In a way we were collaborators – believe me, Mallory, we will be again. I've a lot to tell you ...' Happy to see Mallory, but concerned for the shivering physician, Hinton embraced him with his restless hands. When Mallory flinched, trying to protect his shoulders, Hinton whistled and peered solicitously inside his shirt.

'Mallory, I'm sorry – that police car confused me. They'll be coming for me soon, we have to move fast. But you don't look too well, doctor. Time's running out, I suppose, it's difficult to understand at first . . .'

'I'm starting to. What about you, Hinton? I need to talk to you about everything. You look –'

Hinton grimaced. He slapped his hip, impatient with his under-nourished body, an atrophied organ that he would soon discard. 'I had to starve myself, the wingloading of that machine was so low. It took years, or they might have noticed. Those endless medical checks, they were terrified that I was brewing up an even more advanced psychosis – they couldn't grasp that I was opening the door to a new world.' He gazed round at the space centre, at the empty wind. 'We had to get out of time – that's what the space programme was all about . . .'

He beckoned Mallory towards a steel staircase that led up to the assembly deck six storeys above them. 'We'll go topside. I'm living in the Shuttle – there's a crew module of the Mars platform still inside the hold, a damn sight more comfortable than most of the hotels in Florida.' He added, with an ironic gleam: 'I imagine it's the last place they'll come to look for me.'

Mallory began to climb the staircase. He tried not to touch the greasy rivets and sweating rails, lowering his eyes from the tiled skin of the Shuttle as it emerged above the assembly deck. After all the years of thinking about Cape Kennedy he was still unprepared for the strangeness of this vast, reductive machine, a Juggernaut that could be pushed by its worshippers across the planet, devouring the years and hours and seconds.

Even Hinton seemed subdued, scanning the sky as if waiting for Shepley to appear. He was careful not to turn his back on Mallory, clearly suspecting that the former NASA physician had been sent to trap him.

'Flight and time, Mallory, they're bound together. The birds have always known that. To get out of time we first need to learn to fly. That's why I'm here. I'm teaching myself to fly, going back through all these old planes to the beginning. I want to fly without wings . . .'

As the Shuttle's delta wing fanned out above them, Mallory swayed against the rail. Exhausted by the climb, he tried to pump his lungs. The silence was too great, this stillness at the centre of the stopped clock of the world. He searched the breathless forest and runways for any sign of movement. He needed one of Hinton's machines to take off and go racketting across the sky.

'Mallory, you're going ...? Don't worry, I'll help you through it.' Hinton had taken his elbow and steadied him on his feet. Mallory felt the light suddenly steepen, the intense white glare he had last seen as the cheetah sprang towards him. Time left the air, wavered briefly as he struggled to retain his hold on the passing seconds.

A flock of martins swept across the assembly deck, swirled like exploding soot around the Shuttle. Were they trying to warn him? Roused by the brief flurry, Mallory felt his eyes clear. He had been able to shake off the attack, but it would come again.

'Doctor – ? You'll be all right.' Hinton was plainly disappointed as he watched Mallory steady himself at the rail. 'Try not to fight it, doctor, everyone makes that mistake.'

'It's going ...' Mallory pushed him away. Hinton was too close to the rail, the man's manic gestures could jostle him over the edge. 'The birds –'

'Of course, we'll join the birds! Mallory, we can all fly, every one of us. Think of it, doctor, true flight. We'll live forever in the air!'

'Hinton ...' Mallory backed along the deck as Hinton seized the greasy rail, about to catapult himself on to the wind. He needed to get away from this madman and his lunatic schemes.

Hinton waved to the aircraft below, saluting the ghosts in their cockpits. 'Lilienthal and the Wrights, Curtiss and Bleriot, even old Mignet – they're here, doctor. That's why I came to Cape Kennedy. I needed to go back to the beginning, long before aviation sent us all off on the wrong track. When time stops, Mallory, we'll step from this deck and fly towards the sun. You and I, doctor, and Anne ...'

Hinton's voice was deepening, a cavernous boom. The white flank of the Shuttle's hull was a lantern of translucent bone, casting a spectral light over the sombre forest. Mallory swayed forward, on some half-formed impulse he wanted Hinton to vault the rail, step out on to the air and challenge the birds. If he pressed his shoulders ...

'Doctor – ?'

Mallory raised his hands, but he was unable to draw any nearer to Hinton. Like the cheetah, he was for ever a few inches away.

Hinton had taken his arm in a comforting gesture, urging him towards the rail.

'Fly, doctor ...'

Mallory stood at the edge. His skin had become part of the air, invaded by the light. He needed to shrug aside the huge encumbrance of time and space, this rusting deck and the clumsy tracked vehicle. He could hang free, suspended forever above the forest, master of time and light. He would fly . . .

A flurry of charged air struck his face. Fracture lines appeared in the wind around him. The transparent wings of a powered glider soared past, its propeller chopping at the sunlight.

Hinton's hands gripped his shoulders, bundling him impatiently over the rail. The glider slewed sideways, wheeled and flew towards them again. The sunlight lanced from its propeller, a stream of photons that drove time back into Mallory's eyes. Pulling himself free from Hinton, he fell to his knees as the young woman swept past in her glider. He saw her anxious face behind the goggles, and heard her voice shout warningly at Hinton.

But Hinton had already gone. His feet rang against the metal staircase. As he took off in the Fokker he called out angrily to Mallory, disappointed with him. Mallory knelt by the edge of the steel deck, waiting for time to flow back into his mind, hands gripping the oily rail with the strength of the new-born.

6

Tape 24: *August 17.*
Again, no sign of Hinton today.

Anne is asleep. An hour ago, when I returned from the drugstore, she looked at me with focused eyes for the first time in a week. By an effort I managed to feed her in the few minutes she was fully awake. Time has virtually stopped for her, there are long periods when she is clearly in an almost stationary world, a series of occasionally varying static tableaux. Then she wakes briefly and starts talking about Hinton and a flight to Miami she is going to make with him in his Cessna. Yet she seems refreshed by these journeys into the light, as if her mind is drawing nourishment from the very fact that no time is passing.

I feel the same, despite the infected wound on my shoulder – Hinton's dirty finger-nails. The attacks come a dozen times a day, everything slows to a barely perceptible flux. The intensity of light is growing, photons backing up all the way to the sun. As I left the drugstore I watched a parakeet cross the road over my head, it seemed to take two hours to fly fifty feet.

Perhaps Anne has another week before time stops for her. As for myself, three weeks? It's curious to think that at, say, precisely 3.47

p.m., 8 September, time will stop for ever. A single micro-second will flash past unnoticed for everyone else, but for me will last an eternity. I'd better decide how I want to spend it!

Tape 25: *August 19.*
A hectic two days, Anne had a relapse at noon yesterday, vaso-vagal shock brought on by waking just as Hinton strafed the hotel in his Wright Flyer. I could barely detect her heartbeat, spent hours massaging her calves and thighs (I'd happily go out into eternity caressing my wife). I managed to stand her up, walked her up and down the balcony in the hope that the noise of Hinton's aircraft might jolt her back on to the rails. In fact, this morning she spoke to me in a completely lucid way, obviously appalled by my derelict appearance. For her it's one of those quiet afternoons three weeks ago.

We could still leave, start up one of the abandoned cars and reach the border at Jacksonville before the last minutes run out. I have to keep reminding myself why we came here in the first place. Running north will solve nothing. If there is a solution it's here, some-where between Hinton's obsessions and Shepley's orbiting coffin, between the space centre and those bright, eerie transits that are all too visible at night. I hope I don't go out just as it arrives, spend the rest of eternity looking at the vaporizing corpse of the man I helped to die in space. I keep thinking of that tiger. Somehow I can calm it.

Tape 26: *August 25.*
3.30 p.m. The first uninterrupted hour of conscious time I've had in days. When I woke 15 minutes ago Hinton had just finished strafing the hotel – the palms were shaking dust and insects all over the balcony. Clearly Hinton is trying to keep us awake, postponing the end until he's ready to play his last card, or perhaps until I'm out of the way and he's free to be with Anne.

I'm still thinking about his motives. He seems to have embraced the destruction of time, as if this whole malaise were an opportunity that we ought to seize, the next evolutionary step forward. He was steering me to the edge of the assembly deck, urging me to fly, if Gale Shepley hadn't appeared in her glider I would have dived over the rail. In a strange way he was helping me, guiding me into that new world without time. When he turned Shepley loose from the Shuttle he didn't think he was killing him, but setting him free.

The ever-more primitive aircraft – Hinton's quest for a pure form of flight, which he will embark upon at the last moment. A Santos-

Dumont flew over yesterday, an ungainly box-kite, he's given up his First World War machines. He's deliberately flying badly designed aircraft, all part of his attempt to escape from winged aviation into absolute flight, poetical rather than aeronautical structures.

The roots of shamanism and levitation, and the erotic cathexis of flight – can one see them as an attempt to escape from time? The shaman's supposed ability to leave his physical form and fly with his spiritual body, the psychopomp guiding the souls of the deceased and able to achieve a mastery of fire, together seem to be linked with those defects of the vestibular apparatus brought on by prolonged exposure to zero gravity during the space flights. We should have welcomed them.

That tiger – I'm becoming obsessed with the notion that it's on fire.

Tape 27: *August 28.*

An immense silence today, not a murmur over the soft green deck of Florida. Hinton may have killed himself. Perhaps all this flying is some kind of expiatory ritual, when he dies the shaman's curse will be lifted. But do I want to go back into time? By contrast, that static world of brilliant light pulls at the heart like a vision of Eden. If time *is* a primitive mental structure we're right to reject it. There's a sense in which not only the shaman's but all mystical and religious beliefs are an attempt to devise a world without time. Why did primitive man, who needed a brain only slightly larger than the tiger in Gale's zoo, in fact have a mind almost equal to those of Freud and Leonardo? Perhaps all that surplus neural capacity was there to release him from time, and it has taken the space age, and the sacrifice of the first astronaut, to achieve that single goal.

Kill Hinton ... How, though?

Tape 28: *September 3.*

Missing days. I'm barely aware of the flux of time any longer. Anne lies on the bed, wakes for a few minutes and makes a futile attempt to reach the roof, as if the sky offers some kind of escape. I've just brought her down from the staircase. It's too much of an effort to forage for food, on my way to the supermarket this morning the light was so bright that I had to close my eyes, hand-holding my way around the streets like a blind beggar. I seemed to be standing on the floor of an immense furnace.

Anne is increasingly restless, murmuring to herself in some novel language, as if preparing for a journey. I recorded one of her drawn-out monologues, like some Gaelic love-poem, then speeded it up to normal time. An agonized 'Hinton ... Hinton ...'

It's taken her twenty years to learn.

Tape 29: *September 6.*
There can't be more than a few days left. The dream-time comes on a dozen stretches each day, everything slows to a halt. From the balcony I've just watched a flock of orioles cross the street. They seemed to take hours, their unmoving wings supporting them as they hung above the trees.

At last the birds have learned to fly.

Anne is awake ...

(*Anne*): Who's learned to fly?

(*EM*): It's all right – the birds.

(*Anne*): Did you teach them? What am I talking about? How long have I been away?

(*EM*): Since dawn. Tell me what you were dreaming.

(*Anne*): Is this a dream? Help me up. God, it's dark in the street. There's no time left here. Edward, find Hinton. Do whatever he says.

7

Kill Hinton ...

As the engine of the Yamaha clacked into life, Mallory straddled the seat and looked back at the hotel. At any moment, as if seizing the last few minutes left to her, Anne would leave the bedroom and try to make her way to the roof. The stationary clocks in Titusville were about to tell the real time for her, eternity for this lost woman would be a flight of steps around an empty elevator shaft.

Kill Hinton ... he had no idea how. He set off through the streets to the east of Titusville, shakily weaving in and out of the abandoned cars. With its stiff gearbox and unsteady throttle the Yamaha was exhausting to control. He was driving through an unfamiliar suburb of the town, a terrain of tract houses, shopping malls and car parks laid out for the NASA employees in the building boom of the 1960s. He passed an overturned truck that had spilled its cargo of television sets across the road, and a laundry van that had careened through the window of a liquor store.

Three miles to the east were the gantries of the space centre. An aircraft hung in the air above them, a primitive helicopter with an overhead propeller. The tapering blades were stationary, as if Hinton had at last managed to dispense with wings.

Mallory pressed on towards the Cape, the engine of the motorcycle at full throttle. The tracts of suburban housing unravelled before him, endlessly repeating themselves, the same shopping malls, bars and motels, the same stores and used-car lots that he and Anne had seen in their journey across the continent. He could almost believe that he was driving through Florida again, through the hundreds of small towns that merged together, a suburban universe in which these identical liquor stores, car parks and shopping malls formed the building blocks of a strand of urban DNA generated by the nucleus of the space centre. He had driven down this road, across these silent intersections, not for minutes or hours but for years and decades. The unravelling strand covered the entire surface of the globe, and then swept out into space to pave the walls of the universe before it curved back on itself to land here at its departure point at the space centre. Again he passed the overturned truck beside its scattered television sets, again the laundry van in the liquor store window. He would forever pass them, forever cross the same intersection, see the same rusty sign above the same motel cabin . . .

'Doctor . . . !'

The smell of burning flesh quickened in Mallory's nose. His right calf was pressed against the exhaust manifold of the idling Yamaha. Charred fragments of his cotton trousers clung to the raw wound. As the young woman in the black flying suit ran across the street Mallory pushed himself away from the clumsy machine, stumbled over its spinning wheels and knelt in the road.

He had stopped at an intersection half a mile from the centre of Titusville. The vast planetary plain of parking lots had withdrawn, swirled down some cosmic funnel and then contracted to this small suburban enclave of a single derelict motel, two tract houses and a bar. Twenty feet away the blank screens of the television sets stared at him from the road beside the overturned truck. A few steps further along the sidewalk the laundry van lay in its liquor store window, dusty bottles of vodka and bourbon shaded by the wing-tip of the glider which Gale Shepley had landed in the street.

'Dr Mallory! Can you hear me? Dear man . . .' She pushed back Mallory's head and peered into his eyes, then switched off the still clacking engine of the Yamaha. 'I saw you sitting here, there was something – My God, your leg! Did Hinton . . . ?'

'No ... I set fire to myself.' Mallory climbed to his feet, an arm around the girl's shoulder. He was still trying to clear his head, there was something curiously beguiling about that vast suburban world ... 'I was a fool trying to ride it. I must see Hinton.'

'Doctor, listen to me ...' The girl shook his hands, her eyes wide with fever. Her mascara and hair were even more bizarre than he remembered. 'You're dying! A day or two more, an hour maybe, you'll be gone. We'll find a car and I'll drive you north.' With an effort she took her eyes from the sky. 'I don't like to leave Dad, but you've got to get away from here, it's inside your head now.'

Mallory tried to lift the heavy Yamaha. 'Hinton – it's all that's left now. For Anne, too. Somehow I have to ... kill him.'

'He knows that, doctor –' She broke off at the sound of an approaching aero-engine. An aircraft was hovering over the nearby streets, its shadowy bulk visible through the palm leaves, the flicker of a rotor blade across the sun. As they crouched among the television sets it passed above their heads. An antique autogyro, it lumbered through the air like an aerial harvester, its free-spinning rotor apparently powered by the sunlight. Sitting in the open cockpit, the pilot was too busy with his controls to search the streets below.

Besides, as Mallory knew, Hinton had already found his quarry. Standing on the roof of the hotel, a dressing gown around her shoulders, was Anne Mallory. At last she had managed to climb the stairs, driven on by her dream of the sky. She stared sightlessly at the autogyro, stepping back a single pace only when it circled the hotel and came in to land through a storm of leaves and dust. When it touched down on the roof the draught from its propeller stripped the gown from her shoulders. Naked, she turned to face the autogyro, lover of this strange machine come to save her from a time-reft world.

8

As they reached the NASA causeway huge columns of smoke were rising from the space centre. From the pillion seat of the motorcycle Mallory looked up at the billows boiling into the stained air. The forest was flushed with heat, the foliage glowing like furnace coals.

Had Hinton refuelled the Shuttle's engines and prepared the craft for lift-off? He would take Anne with him, and cast them both loose into space as he had done with Shepley, joining the dead astronaut in his orbital bier.

Smoke moved through the trees ahead of them, driven by the

explosions coming from the launch site of the Shuttle. Gale throttled back the Yamaha and pointed to a break in the clouds. The Shuttle still sat on its platform, motors silent, the white hull reflecting the flash of explosions from the concrete runways.

Hinton had set fire to his antique planes. Thick with oily smoke, the flames lifted from the glowing shells slumped on their undercarts. The Curtiss biplane was burning briskly. A frantic blaze devoured the engine compartment of the Fokker, detonated the fuel tank and set off the machine-gun ammunition. The exploding cartridges kicked through the wings as they folded like a house of cards.

Gale steadied the Yamaha with her feet, and skirted the glowing trees two hundred yards from the line of incandescent machines. The explosions flashed in her goggles, blanching her vivid make-up and giving her blond hair an ash-like whiteness. The heat flared against Mallory's sallow face as he searched the aircraft for any sign of Hinton. Fanned by the flames that roared from its fuselage, the autogyro's propeller rotated swiftly, caught fire and spun in a last blazing carnival. Beside it, flames raced along the wings of the Wright Flyer, in a shower of sparks the burning craft lifted into the air and fell on to its back upon the red-hot hulk of the Sopwith Camel. Ignited by the intense heat, the primed engine of the Flying Flea roared into life, propelled the tiny aircraft in a scurrying arc among the burning wrecks, setting off the Spad and Bleriot before it overturned in a furnace of rolling flame.

'Doctor – on the assembly deck!'

Mallory followed the girl's raised hand. A hundred feet above them, Anne and Hinton stood side by side on the metal landing of the stairway. The flames from the burning aircraft wavered against their faces, as if they were already moving through the air together. Although Hinton's arm was around Anne's waist, they seemed unaware of each other when they stepped forward into the light.

9

As always during his last afternoons at Cocoa Beach, Mallory rested by the swimming pool of the abandoned hotel, watching the pale glider float patiently across the undisturbed skies of Cape Kennedy. In this peaceful arbour, surrounded by the drowsing inmates of the zoo, he listened to the fountain cast its crystal gems on to the grass beside his chair. The spray of water was now almost stationary, like the glider and the wind and the watching cheetahs, elements of an emblematic and glowing world.

As time slipped away from him, Mallory stood under the fountain, happy to see it transform itself into a glass tree that shed an opalescent fruit on to his shoulders and hands. Dolphins flew through the air over the nearby sea. Once he immersed himself in the pool, delighted to be embedded in this huge block of condensed time.

Fortunately, Gale Shepley had rescued him before he drowned. Mallory knew that she was becoming bored with him. She was intent now only on the search for her father, confident that he would soon be returning from the tideways of space. At night the trajectories were ever lower, tracks of charged particles that soared across the forest. She had almost ceased to eat, and Mallory was glad that once her father arrived she would at last give up her flying. Then the two of them would leave together.

Mallory had made his own preparations for departure. The key to the tiger cage he held always in his hand. There was little time left to him now, the light-filled world had transformed itself into a series of tableaux from a pageant that celebrated the founding days of creation. In the finale every element in the universe, however humble, would take its place on the stage in front of him.

He watched the tiger waiting for him at the bars of its cage. The great cats, like the reptiles before them, had always stood partly out of time. The flames that marked its pelt reminded him of the fire that had consumed the aircraft at the space centre, the fire through which Anne and Hinton still flew forever.

He left the pool and walked towards the tiger cage. He would unlock the door soon, embrace these flames, lie down with this beast in a world beyond time.

David Constantine

Six Poems

DAVID CONSTANTINE was born in 1944 in Salford, Lancashire. He read Modern Languages at Wadham College, Oxford, where he wrote a doctoral thesis on the work of the German poet Friedrich Hölderlin. In 1969 he became a lecturer in German at Durham University, and in 1981 took up his present post of Fellow in German at the Queen's College, Oxford. He has had two collections of poetry published by Bloodaxe Books: *A Brightness to Cast Shadows* (1980) and *Watching for Dolphins* (1983). His first novel *Davies* will be published in 1984.

Pillbox

*D*ome of the sun. So we shall burn
   Immured in a head, peering through hyphens.
   Though we are prickly with angles of vision
An intelligence may calculate our blindspots
A hand rise out of the earth
To post us flames. Somebody squats
On the skull with a trepan
Where our flailing glances cannot dislodge him.
The surf is placid at nights
And soothing the scent of camomile.
We have nailed this coast. Buried to the eyeballs
We shall burn like lampions.
The quenching Atlantic will back away from us.

Thoughts of the Commandant of the Fortress
of St-Vaast-la-Hougue

My boy keeps up appearances.
He props the dead soldiers in their embrasures
And fires their muskets from time to time.

By candle-light in the nucleus
With a bitten finger I patrol our miles of walls
Hearing at every turn the claws of a grapnel
Or the moat bleeding away through a wound.

And what is worse: low tide when we
Padlock our throat and cordon the slit with salt
And the birds stalk over the foetid mud
Bayoneting the overturned soft crustaceans?

Or full: when we are brimming with fear
That our besiegers thus will fall quietly upon us
With the soft wings and the demon faces of moths?

They have surrendered oceans of freedom to beat these walls.
How furious will be their disappointment
After the falling silent of my ragged bird-scarer.

Zerlina

Waking this morning I was someone else:
A wife who knows she has conceived, but the shock
I felt under the heart was remembering how he struck
The strings with the backs of his fingers and my new pulse
Was the starting again of his singing in my veins
Sotto voce. I have gone about the house
And to and fro in the garden hearing his damned voice
All day under my clothes carrying his tunes.

He swung my soul, he showed me how they move
In very presence, those whom an innocent love
Flings to the dance. And I believed his tongue,
I swallowed him, we married there and then.
I am his lawful widow big with song.
I have danced all day, believing him again.

Leporello

Forked in her moorish arches, standing sentry,
I watched the summer heavens teeming down;
I dozed under her generous balcony,
Dopey with orange blossom and moonshine,
Hearing their silly laughter above my head,
His rapier clattering to the marble floor,
Rustle and sigh of things of hers discarded,
A rose thrown over into my lamplight square.
When he came down I kissed his ungloved hands
And we escaped then through the skirting gardens.
Once, in the wolf's clothing, using his voice,
I drew his starved wife down. Inhaled the perfume
Of an amorous woman, saw the abandoned face
That hurt my eyes even through my borrowed plume.

Nestor encourages the Troops
(after *Iliad*, ii, 336ff)

My dears, you sound like little boys
Still pimply before they redden out
With bloodlust. Who promised then? Did not
We all with drink and a handshake
Cross our hearts and hope to die
For Agamemnon? Yapping, though we yap
Till kingdom come, will get us nowhere. Sir,
Lead them cheerfully back on to
The killing-ground and let
The one or two malingerers, the schemers
For early home-time, the impiously
Unwaiting to hear God's final word, let them
Drop dead. I personally
Believe we were given the nod and the wink
That day by Zeus. It lightened, did it not,
Righthandedly when we were boarding
Our snouted ships for Troy. Well then
For Helen's misdemeanours and your wasted years
Anticipate a just desert
Of married Trojan cunt. When we are in
And the pretty fires are burning and only toddlers
And snivelling old men encumber your knees
Remember then you thought of going home. However
If luxury to come (shitting on silks)
Will not embolden you try running and we,
Your lords, will stick you to the ships.

Adam confesses an infidelity to Eve

I dreamed you were stolen from my left side
And woke hugging the pain. There in our room
Lit by the street lamp she appeared to me
Like something pulled from the earth. She is bulb-white;

Her shadowy place as black as wet moss
Or the widow spider. Believe me
She flattened my raised hands. She gripped
The cage of my heart between her knees,

Gluttonous for mandrake, and fed then,
Crammed her nether mouth, so rooting at
My evasive tongue I feared she would swallow it.
Curtained together under her hair

Only when she rose from drinking
And rolled and bucked as though I were reined
Did I see her face, like a slant moon,
Her eyes smudged and cavernous, her mouth bruised.

She cried like a seal. When she bowed down
Her brow on mine as savages pray
Enshrining my head between her forearms
Then, I confess, feeling her cold tears

I lapped them from her cheeks and let her rest.
My seed ran out of her, cold. On the street
Hissing with rain the lamps were extinguished.
You, when I woke, lay hooped on my left arm.

Alasdair Gray

The Liberation

ALASDAIR GRAY is a middle-aged Glaswegian pedestrian. His published books are *Lanark*, a novel, and *Unlikely Stories, Mostly*, a collection of unlikely stories, mostly. His next novel, *1982, Janine*, from which this extract is taken, will be published in 1984 by Jonathan Cape and in 1985 by Penguin.

Our lives in the house where I was born were comfortable but depressed. The depression was equally shared so we did not notice it. I only once heard my parents laugh and never heard them raise their voices in anger, or complain, or weep. The only one to raise his voice in our house was Old Red when he denounced the capitalist class or talked Utopian, which was why Mum and I disliked him. We knew that most families were noisier than us, but also felt that noise was abnormal and unhealthy. We believed very few people were as normal and healthy as us.

This is how I came to make them laugh.

I was seventeen and had sat an entrance exam for the Glasgow Royal Technical College. I still went to school, though the teaching would only have value if I failed that exam and had to try another. Leaving home in the morning I sometimes met the postman in the street and said, 'Anything for me?', and one day, from the bundle in his hand, he extracted a buff official envelope with my name on it, the first letter addressed to me in my life. I placed it carefully in my pocket. Instead of going to school I took the colliery road which led down through the skirts of the town to a bridge over the river, and then I turned along a track through the wood on the further bank. My heart was thudding very slow and hard. I was sure I had passed the exam, but how well had I done? The day was close and warm, the sky a ceiling of smooth grey cloud with no hint of rain. I left the track and climbed a steep path through bracken and bluebells and came to a flat place surrounded by birks and rowans under an overhanging rock. William Wallace was supposed to have hidden here from the English but most Scottish towns have an obscure corner where that is supposed to have happened. The place was better known because on Sunday nights some miners called the Boghead crowd used it for illegal games of pitch-and-toss. I sat on a low boulder, read my letter and sighed with relief. I had done well in the exam. Excitement gripped my legs. I left the boulder and waded uphill through the bracken by no path at all, delighting to feel my body break and tread underfoot the resistance of the fronds. Fifteen minutes later I paused, slightly breathless, and looked back. This part of the country was a sort of fertile plateau through which the river carved a steep valley, so the high land was good pasture and cornfield, the low ground was wooded and shaggy. Facing me, on a ridge across the river, lay the whole length of the long town: a quarter-mile terrace of but-and-ben cottages in the east, a centre of two-storey houses where the shops, pubs and cinema were, a row of mansions and bungalows standing in their own gardens, and a council estate of semi-detached villas in the west. All this, with the railway station, four schools, four churches, cast-iron swings and roundabout in the park, should have seemed familiar because I knew it thoroughly, but it did not look familiar. It looked queer and lonely, because I was going to leave it.

I wandered about the town all morning, mostly in the outskirts, sometimes in the main street, and every ordinary friendly thing from the monkey-puzzle tree on the Church of Scotland manse lawn to a fat old cat basking on a sill had that queer foreign look. I stared a long time at an advert in a chemist's shop. It showed tall white identical castles receding to a horizon. Before them a knight in white armour held a shield labelled GIBBS TOOTHPASTE and waved a triumphant sword over a batwinged reptile labelled *Dragon Decay*. A slogan somewhere said

> GIBBS IN THE MORNING,
> GIBBS IN THE NIGHT,
> KEEPS EVERY CASTLE
> SHINING AND BRIGHT.
> (Your teeth are every castle.)

I had known that advert for years, why? Nowadays companies change their displays, slogans, packets and products continually, they spend millions on advertising to stop the government taking it in taxation. My seventeenth year was closer to the time of thrift and rationing when only the government spent money on adverts, adverts which told us to buy as little as possible. MAKE DO AND MEND they said, above a picture of a cheerful housewife sewing a patch on her husband's jacket, DIG FOR VICTORY, above the husband planting cabbages on his suburban lawn, HOLIDAY AT HOME! IS YOUR JOURNEY REALLY NECESSARY? That daft toothpaste advert had been in the window since 1940 and had entered my daydreams. I still sometimes wore the armour, rescued Jane Russell from the dragon and, finding her ungrateful and treacherous, chained her up in those castles. But I was not daydreaming now. I was asking the advert, 'Will I remember you when I'm gone? Will you remember me when I'm gone?' and the answer, 'Probably not,' confused and puzzled me, though I was too excited to feel depressed. I stared an equally long time at a three-foot high marble soldier in puttees, cape and round pudding-basin helmet, his hands clasped and head bowed over a grounded rifle. He stood on a pillar carved with the names of over two hundred men from the town and its surroundings who had died in the first world war. A recent bronze plate listed an additional forty killed in the second world war. *Their Name Liveth For Evermore*, was inscribed above the lists, and *Lest We Forget* underneath, and I could not connect the inscriptions, which seemed to deny each other. The two wars did not interest me but I suddenly wished that the soldiers who had fought and survived them were also listed, for then I could have read my father's name.

I arrived home for dinner at twelve-thirty as if I had just come from school and said nothing about the letter. I kept my mouth shut till later that evening when we were all gathered round the table for tea. This was usually a meat or fish course with bread, biscuits, cakes and (of course) a big pot of tea. Dad received, in addition, the remains of the soup or pudding Mum and I ate at dinner-time. Half-way through the meal tonight Dad said, as I expected he would, 'I wonder when we'll hear from the Technical College.'

I said casually, 'I got the letter this morning.'

A fork with a bit of potato on the prongs stopped still for five whole seconds in front of Dad's open mouth and was then laid down carefully on his plate. He said, 'Well?'

'I've passed,' said I, calmly continuing to eat.

He said, 'Passed have you? Good! But what's wrong? What are you trying to hide?'

'Nothing,' said I, and handed him the letter. He read it with a face wrinkled and concentrated in a great worried frown while Mum turned her startled stare from me to him. He laid down the letter, tilted his head back and made a dry, hacking noise like this: 'AKHA! AKHA! AKHA! AKHA!'

My mother cried out, '*What's wrong?*'

He said, 'Wrong? He's sixth best out of two hundred and eighty-two applicants! He's sixth best in the whole west of Scotland!'

My mother chuckled, left her seat and cuddled me and I cuddled her back. Then she got embarrassed and pulled away. If I had not surprised her with my news she would never have cuddled me. Dad was grinning and shaking his fist at me and saying again and again, 'Ye buggar! Ye buggar! Ye buggar!' — so I allowed myself a small smile. If I had proudly told him the news when he came in from work he would have given that small smile and said something like, 'Fine! You arenae the best, but you certainly are not the worst.' Like most parents he did not want his child to openly display pride and happiness, because these states make other people envious, and often go before a fall. By hiding my feelings I had tricked him into showing his, and had risen above him.

My parents had been paying a weekly sum into a Scottish Co-operative insurance scheme which could be realized after my sixteenth birthday. It was devised to help working-class children across the gap between their schooling and their employment, and as I now needed new clothes for the technical college, and as I had stopped growing, my parents decided to spend the whole sum on clothes which would last till I was fully self-supporting. At the time I thought this decision perfectly natural though now it astonishes me. Since setting up house together they had lived carefully on less than twelve pounds a week, where did they get the courage to dispose of two or three hundred pounds in less than ten days? They must have been mad, as mad as a woman I overheard in a London bank. She wore a smart leather trouser-suit and in a loud hooting voice said to a friend, 'It cost me nine hundred pounds. I couldn't possibly afford it of course but we must be extravagant sometimes, just to cheer ourselves up.'

She could afford it alright. Part of her knew that the price of that suit was the weekly take-home wage of six railwaymen working overtime or twenty families on the dole, so her delight in extravagance came from feeling superior to the rest of the world, superior to fate. I hope my parents felt some of that delight as they discussed spending the equivalent of half their yearly income on my wardrobe. If so they excused the feeling by pretending they were completing a job of work. They had produced a brain which the Scottish Education Department had stamped 'First Class'. Now they would post to the world in a suitable packet. Hitherto my mother had chosen all my clothes, so we were surprised when suddenly Dad uttered forceful opinions. 'A made-to-measure single-breasted suit of the best-quality Harris tweed is a . . . a . . . a . . . timeless garment. The style of it has remained virtually unchanged for well over half a century. American businessmen wear it to conferences. Highland crofters wear it to church. A British working man can wear it anywhere without appearing a traitor to his class.'

'Made-to-measure suits are very dear,' said my mother, 'and not at all necessary. An off-the-peg suit may not fit Jock perfectly but I'm a good enough needlewoman to adjust it, as you well know.'

'I will prove to you,' said my father, taking such care to speak slowly and quietly that we knew he was greatly excited, 'I will prove to you that a made-to-measure suit of the sort I am imagining will be the best possible economy. In off-the-peg suits the trousers wear out long before the jackets do. They must! If a man is not crawling on his knees like a collier or humping weights on his back like a dustman then the part of his anatomy which suffers most wear is the seat. I am certain that – other things being equal – the life-expectancy of the trousers of an off-the-peg suit is less than half that of the jacket. But those who bespeak a suit from a good tailor can order all the trousers they want, which is another instance of the rich spending less money in the long run through their ability to be lavish in the first place.'

'So you want us to buy the lad a jacket and two pair of trousers in the same cloth.'

'No!' said Dad, 'I want us to buy him three jackets and three waist-coats and seven pairs of trousers and two overcoats of the same cloth! Let him change his trousers every day of the week. The fabric will suffer so little strain that with ordinary care it will look continually smart and last him a lifetime.'

Mum said firmly, 'I have never heard a more ridiculous suggestion. Why buy the lad a lot of nice clothes if we don't give him some variety? Jock needs a couple of ordinary suits for everyday wear, one in a medium grey check and one in brown. And he needs a dark suit for formal occasions and a blazer and flannels for sunny weather and holidays. I can see the sense in two trousers to a jacket, yes, fine, but seven identical trousers and three identical jackets are utterly daft.'

Dad replied in the cautious, downcast but obstinate tone he used when speaking of sexual matters.

'I do recognize that a variety of clothing is biologically essential to women, especially to the young ones, because they use clothes to draw attention to themselves, and men (younger men) like them for that. But what an employer values in a man – what a man values in his workmates – what a man values in himself – is consistency. If Jock goes to Glasgow equipped as I suggest he will impress his teachers and workmates and prospective bosses with a neat, simple, consistent appearance bordering upon the miraculous. The material of the suit I have in mind is dark enough to wear at a funeral but not dark enough to suggest one, so with the right colour of necktie it can be worn on any occasion. In rough work situations, of course, it will be protected by overalls. But I agree that he requires a blazer and flannels for especially sunny days. We don't get many of these.'

Mum said firmly, 'The idea is ridiculous. People will laugh at the boy.'

Dad said, 'I doubt that.'

They could not agree so I was in a position to adjudicate. Like most seventeen-year-olds I had very little sense of my own identity, so the idea of striking a mysteriously consistent note in the turmoil of Glasgow appealed to me. I opted for six trousers, three jackets, two waistcoats and an overcoat of the same cloth, and a black dinner jacket with matching trousers, and the blazer and the flannels.

The suit was ordered from a tailor in Kilmarnock and after the second fitting we visited a haberdasher to get socks, shirts and underwear. Since Dad had gained most of his own way in the matter of the suit he agreed completely with my mother's choice of the other things, so my wishes were not consulted before we came to the necktie counter. The salesman displayed ties of silk and cotton and wool in a great many patterns and colours. My mother fingered them, held them up and laid several aside before it occurred to her to ask, 'Have you any idea of what *you* would like, Jock?'

I pointed to a rack of bow ties and said, 'I would like those.' Mum and Dad stared hard at me and then at each other. They were alarmed. Bow ties in those days — perhaps even nowadays — were worn by professional people in risky businesses like horse-racing, the arts and journalism. University lecturers who courted publicity often wore bow ties. My mother said, 'Are you sure you want one of those?'

'I want them all like that.'

'But is it *important* to you?'

I shrugged and said, 'The money you are spending is not mine so I'll wear whatever you buy. But you asked what sort of tie I would like, and now you know.'

There was a look of helpless worry on her face which cut me to the heart. She said faintly, 'What colour?'

I said, 'I leave that entirely to you.'

The only bow ties without vivid patterns were wine red or dark blue, so she bought half a dozen of the dark blue, then returned to the shirt counter and changed my dozen white shirts for pale blue ones, so they would match. My father, for political reasons, would have preferred a red tie, but a red tie on a white shirt was too strikingly radical even for him, and a pink shirt for a man was unthinkable. It hinted at homosexual tastes which in those days were downright criminal.

I cannot remember what weather lay over the streets and houses of the town when the train took me away from it. Mum and Dad saw me to the station and we said very little before the train pulled out. Beyond the station the line curved across the valley on a high viaduct, and a minute later I could look back and see two tiny figures on the end of the station platform, one with a flickering white speck attached to it. Either Mum or Dad was waving a handkerchief. By the time I had pulled out my own hanky and lowered the carriage window some trees had come between us. I shut the window, crossed my legs carefully to avoid injuring the trouser-crease, folded my arms across the neat new waistcoat, sunk my chin on to the tie and was perplexed by a total absence of feelings. I knew I would be revisiting the long town, but in an essential way I had left it forever and I did not care. I thought that perhaps, in Glasgow, when I was a lonely unit among a million others, a toothpaste advert or a face in the street might bring back childhood memories on a big warm wave of nostalgia. But this never happened. Yes, at first I was very lonely in Glasgow but I enjoyed that. Loneliness felt like freedom. I was sure it would lead to something exciting, something with sex in it. With a pang of guilt I decided that my childhood, apart from a few infantile memories, had been a depressing business and I was better away from it.

My parents had found me lodgings on Paisley Road West in the home of a dependable motherly woman who would tell them if anything went wrong with me. I soon shifted to the flat of a young law student in Hillhead who did not care what went wrong with his lodgers, as long as they paid the rent and did not fight each other. At college I had difficulty at first with the purely mathematical functions, but after six weeks I suddenly realized the almost complete congruency between these and the practical work, and had no trouble with my exams after that. In the Tech refectory I sometimes ate at the same table as Alan. One day, when that table was full up Alan said, 'Make room for Jock,' and tilting his chair on its back legs he stretched an arm across and grabbed an empty chair from a table near by. So I knew we were friends. And then I met Denny.

The women behind the serving hatch in the refectory had always been pleasantly chatty, but one day I noticed a new girl who seemed to actively hate me. She was small and chubby with a moony petulant face which she turned away while serving me, and when I handed her the money she took it with a disdain which suggested I was the filthiest man in the world. I found this upsetting because I had been perfectly polite. Next day when I approached the hatch one of the other women called out, 'Denny! Here's Jock.'

She served me in exactly the same way, except that this time she refused to take my money at all but scurried sideways and started serving someone else. I laid the coins on the counter and went away feeling puzzled. She served me the third day with the same averted face, placing the food on my plate more slowly. Before passing it to me, with the fearful look of someone forcing themselves to jump across a dangerous gap, she bit her lip, hesitated and whispered 'Rotten weather.'

I said 'Yes it is,' and held out the money. She gave an obstinate little shake of the head and hurried to the next customer. The other serving ladies smiled at each other and I left the hatch feeling I had been made to look foolish. I now knew that I attracted her, but she did not attract me. My notions of female attraction were based on Jane Russell and various fashion photographs. I was ignorant. But walking back to Hillhead that evening I began to feel different. It occurred to me that Denny might let me do anything I wanted with her and the thought made me dizzy. I had never, never, never believed that a woman could desire a man. The universal habit of marriage showed that they needed men, but folk often need what they don't want and want what they don't need. My sexual daydreams were full of capture and bondage because I could imagine no other way of keeping a woman I wanted. Denny had no place in the world of my imagination yet I found myself walking faster till I was almost running, and when I reached the lodgings I had decided that next day I would ask her out. But a fortnight passed before I asked her out. In the evenings I walked the streets past couples standing in cinema queues and troops of girls hurrying to the dance-halls, and now the only fact which fed my strong feeling of a great good time coming was the fact of Denny. But next day the sight of her in the refectory completely chilled me. She looked too small and ordinary to associate with enormous desires and satisfactions – she was exactly the same height as myself. Not that she was an ugly girl. When she did not notice I was near she joked brightly with the other students, who were fond of her, and she looked pretty on these occasions. But whenever I came near she lost all confidence and behaved like a young school-girl in front of a ferocious headmaster. This did not please me at all. I desperately wished I knew some other women. Alan said, 'You ought to be nicer to Denny. She's a beautiful piece. If you made her happy she would operate with an astonishing absence of friction. And you need a woman.'

I said, 'I don't like her voice. It sounds cheap and tinny.'

He sighed and said, 'Then think of her from the economic stand-point. She not only refuses to let you pay for your meals, she now refuses to let your friends pay for theirs. This won't last for ever if you don't encourage her a bit. She loves you.'

But only the coldest sort of sexual frustration drove me to Denny in the end. I lay at night in bed haunted by the imaginings which seemed thin and futile. I could no longer take Jane Russell seriously. So when one day Denny whispered, in her fearful jumping-over-a-precipice voice, 'What do you do in the evenings?' I said, 'Will you meet me tonight?'

She nodded and said 'Mhm.'

I said, 'What about seven o'clock at the front entrance?'

She said, 'Aye, alright.'

She did not look happier, she looked slightly more worried and resigned than usual. I left the serving hatch thinking, 'The bitch! She doesn't like me but she certainly wants it. Alright, I'll give it to her.' I had the shallowest notion of what 'it' was – a minute of naked grappling and kissing followed by a minute of slotting together and pumping was all I could conceive. And I was completely wrong about Denny. She wanted me, not 'it', but accepted that 'it' was the price she must pay for my company.

My heart sank when I saw her that evening. The cheaply fashion-able dress she wore was wrong for her kind of shape, and though she had taken a deal of trouble with her hair and lipstick the result was not successful. But she looked cheerful and hopeful for a change, and when we started walking she slipped an arm through mine, and the part of my arm and body which touched her felt warm and secure.

Only my head was irritable with her appearance beside me, so I took her into the dark of a picture-house and we kissed and cuddled in the back row of the stalls among several similar couples. This was not satisfying. My furtive squeezing and fumbling brought none of the quick passionate excitement I sometimes saw enacted on the screen before us, so when we came out at nine-thirty I said, 'Are you coming home with me?'

She said miserably, 'I'd like to, but I don't want to get into trouble.'

I said, 'I'm not a fool Denny. I know what precautions to take.'

She said, 'It's not that. You see I live in a hostel where they lock the doors at ten. If I'm not back before then I get into trouble.'

I said grimly, 'So this is the end of our evening, is it?'

I stared at her accusingly until she whispered, 'Mibby I could say I missed the tram and spent the night with a girlfriend.'

I said, 'Fine!' and steered her firmly by the arm to Cowcaddens Underground, but when I got her into my room off Hyndland Road I was nearly paralysed by embarrassment and worry, because I had never before been all alone with a woman. I coped by behaving almost as if I was completely alone. I made a supper of toasted cheese and cocoa (for two instead of one), ate and drank mine, then brushed my teeth, and wound up the clock, and carefully undressed, folding each article of clothing into its proper place. She sat watching all this with an empty cocoa mug clutched on her lap. I did not put on my pyjamas. I took a contraceptive from a packet, showed it to her and climbed into bed saying, 'Come on Denny, we arenae doing anything unusual.'

She said in a wobbly voice, 'Can I put the light out?'

I said 'Please yourself.'

She switched the light off and undressed. Meanwhile I managed, with much fumbling, to fit the sheath on to my wholly flaccid penis. Then I felt her cold body slip in beside mine and we lay together for a long time. I was waiting to be possessed by a demon of desire which would inspire me to seize and pierce her. This did not happen, though the chill gradually left her skin. I wondered if I was impotent, then remembered how often I masturbated. I wondered if Denny was getting impatient, and if I was perhaps a suppressed homosexual. Would she tell the other refectory women next morning how useless I was in bed? She sighed and snuggled more deeply into my side, and a moment later I noticed she was asleep. I thankfully pulled off the sheath and fell asleep also.

*

I woke before dawn to find our bodies intimately twined although Denny was still sleeping. For half an hour I lay wholly comfortable and at peace, though I regretted that this was not a sexual feeling. I could not help being ignorant. My sexual ideas came from films and books and jokes which all showed love as quick climaxes, because they had to describe it faster than people did it. The alarm clock rang and we got up and dressed on opposite sides of the bed without looking at each other. I heard her say thoughtfully, 'No harm done, anyway.'

I said nothing. I did not know what to think or feel about what had or had not been done. She said, 'Mind you, I'll be crying my eyes out before tonight.'

'Why?'

'The matron of the hostel where I stay takes herself very seriously. A girl who isnae in on time can say she's sorry till she's blue in the face, but matron is never satisfied till she sees the tears.'

I thought of Hislop who was never satisfied until he had dammed the tears up. The world seemed a terribly queer place. I made a breakfast of bacon, eggs, toast and tea and we talked while eating it.

'My Daddy was not very nice to my Mammy but I think he's dead now. We havenae seen him for years. Good riddance to bad rubbish, I say. My Mammy's alright, but she sometimes takes funny turns. And when she takes one of her funny turns she has to go into hospital and I have to go to the hostel.'

'Have you no relations you could live with?'

'Hundreds, but I wouldnae live with scruff like thon.'

It turned out that our birthdays were in the same week, a coincidence which struck her as miraculous. I learned she was sixteen years old. I had thought she was older than me and much more experienced. I was glad I had not seduced her, for she had enough trouble in her life. I avoided travelling into college with her that morning by telling her my first lecture was at eleven, which was a lie. We separated without making plans.

But in the following days her manner when we met at the serving hatch was relaxed and cheerful. She seemed now to think we were connected. I did not tell Alan I had taken her out, but in the dinner queue he once glanced from her to me and murmured, 'Excellent.' We were connected. I could not forget the smooth comforting warmth of her body when I had wakened with her. I lay awake at night, wanting it again. I became very angry with myself. I said, 'You idiot! You don't need comfort, what you need is –' here I hesitated, rejecting 'ecstasy' as too romantic – 'What you need is fun,' and I masturbated, but that did not help. Masturbation was a substitute for ecstasy but no substitute for the comfort of a smooth warm body that liked me. So on Friday I said, 'I'll see you tomorrow at one o'clock.'

She nodded and said 'Mhm.'

Her appearance in the street was as disappointing as the first time. I took her home with me at once and when we got inside the room I said, 'Please come to bed with me Denny,' and was surprised to notice my voice was humble and pleading. It surprised Denny too. She said wonderingly, 'Don't worry, Jock.'

We undressed and got into bed and cuddled for an hour or two. Nobody ever had a skin which was smoother and sleeker than Denny's so it was easy for us to slide and swim all over and around and under each other, though we had sometimes to stop and disentangle the bed-clothes. The palm of my hand still remembers the exact shape of her foot, a small soft globe blending into a larger squarer globe (there cannot be a square globe, yes there was) a soft globe blending into larger squarer globe with five little crisp globes along an edge. Her body was all smooth tight soft globes (how can tight be soft? It was) soft smooth tight globes like silken dumplings blending into each other at the wrist ankle knee elbow breast thigh waist blending in lovely curving creases which a fingertip exactly fitted. Sometimes I said, 'Are you tired of this yet?' and she said, 'No, not yet.'

I took her out for a meal and no longer cared if her dress looked poor and her lipstick wrong. I was so dazzled by my knowledge of her body that I could not face her and kept blushing and keeking sideways at the floor. I had meant to take her to a cinema after the meal, but when I whispered, 'Can we go back and do more of that?' she said, 'Don't worry Jock, it does no harm.'

I wondered if I had invented a completely new and harmless sort of love-making that could go on forever because it was never satisfied. And when, later that evening, I saw her on to the tram which would take her to the south side where her hostel was, I felt very pleasantly exhausted. 'See you on Monday,' I called, waving cheerfully, and the tram moved off and I turned to walk home and

and I was embarrassed by the first continuous erection I ever experienced. It happened suddenly and would not go away. It made walking difficult and I could not stop it. I was not thinking lustfully of Denny or anyone else when this happened, I was not thinking at all, I was stupefied to find that my body had a memory and will of which my mind knew nothing. With a few respites this erection lasted till the following Monday. It was a pain, but a pain I was pleased to suffer, and if I had known the address of Denny's hostel I would have phoned her at once and asked her over to share it. When I saw her on Monday morning and said, 'We must meet tonight,' she said, 'Sure,' with something of her old, worried look, so my manner must have changed a little. When we got to bed I slipped on a sheath and we cuddled and I entered her quickly and easily. I was so glad to be inside that I lay perfectly still. It was she who started moving, so I moved too, to be companionable. I kept stopping whenever the excitement became very great. I feared that if I ejaculated I would go small and feeble and would have to leave her. I had ejaculated several times a week since I was twelve and felt there was no future in it. But I did ejaculate at last, and we slept, then woke and made more love, and slept, and woke and made more love, and slept. Then I heard the alarm ringing, and Denny was sitting up and saying dolefully, 'It'll be the tears again for me tonight.'

I said, 'Why don't you get a room of your own?'

She said, 'How could I?'

I thought hard for a while. I asked what her wages were. She got not quite three pounds a week, which is about twenty-four pounds in modern money, enough to buy food and rent a cheap room if she shared it, but with almost nothing left for entertainment, clothing or transport. In the catering and cleaning businesses employers could and still do pay such money to women of all ages, because these women live with a parent or husband or in a hostel, like Denny, and of course they have little or no union. She said, 'The hostel isnae a bad place, I mean, it's clean and there's quite a good crowd of girls there. Most of them are dead ignorant, like me, but we have some great laughs together.'

I said, 'You've got relations.'

'Well?'

'If you said you were going to live with them, would they take you?'

'Sure, but I'm not going to live with thon scruff.'

'You could pretend to go and live with them but come and stay here.'

'Could I?'

'My landlord spends the weekends at his parents' house. If you don't swagger about the place as if you own it, and if you keep out of the kitchen and stay in this room as much as possible he won't bother us. And then we can be together as much as we like.'

Denny looked worried, then smiled, then looked worried again, and I noticed I was in danger of proposing marriage. We went to the college together, sitting side by side in the underground and holding hands. When we went our separate ways my penis stiffened again and I felt a ring of tightness throb around the top of it as if Denny was still moving there. This invisible wedding ring was with me all that day. I have never felt it since.

Was Denny a virgin before she met me? I entered her very easily and do not think I gave her pain, but breaking a hymen cannot always be a dramatic event. Was there blood on the sheets afterward? Perhaps. My sheets were often bloodstained because Denny did not mind making love when menstruating and her blood was not a kind of dirt which disgusted me. I did not notice if the sheets were stained the first time, I was too occupied to care. I was unusually lucky. I could easily have met a girl whose notion of love-making was as muddled and impatient as my own, a girl who felt obliged to hurry herself and hurry me into some sort of climax. She would probably have succeeded, and that pleasant but inadequate experience would have been the pattern of my future love-making. Maybe Denny's sexual wisdom came from some lucky earlier experiences, but perhaps she was able to give and take delight easily because she did not think enough about sex to turn it into a problem. There are such women. They are seldom glamorous or clever, they are not promiscuous, being usually married to self-satisfied chaps who do not notice why they are well-off; but though few men enjoy the favours of these women we are always glad to see them. They prove that the pain of love is not inevitable but merely the frequentest sort of bad luck.

Not long after this Denny spent a night with me again, then came to live with me under the conditions I had suggested. She had her own key to the flat, but hid this from the landlord and his other lodger by ringing the doorbell before using it. If one of them opened to her she said, 'Is Jock in?' and if they said, 'No,' she scurried past them into my room saying, 'I'll just wait for him, then.'

They found this amusing because she spent more time in that room than I did. I got more pleasure with her than with anyone else but I was afraid people would notice this and think I depended on her. I was afraid she would think that, so when I went out in the evening saying, 'I'll be back by nine,' I would usually be back by nine, but sometimes stayed out till ten, and on these occasions she greeted my return with as much heartfelt relief as if she had feared I would never return. She must have been lonely in that room with only the wireless for company, but I did not like being with her in the streets. The faces of people walking toward us often had a soft, amused, wondering expression which I found annoyingly condescending. Once, coming out of a cinema, a gang of adolescent boys followed us almost the whole way home, laughing and chanting, 'Hairy pie! Hairy pie! Who's got his hairy pie?'

Denny clutched my arm tight and kept hissing, 'Pay no attention! Pay no attention!' as if she feared I would turn round and attack them.

We sometimes quarrelled, of course. I was neat and she was messy. She could not be an hour in a place without disarranging something and shedding wisps of hair, a kirby-grip, a safety-pin or a lipstick-case. Though she worked in a refectory she was not a good cook, so I made the meals and expected her to clean up afterward. There were never many dirty dishes, but she would bustle about in a busy, unsystematic way for half an hour, and when she sat down there would always be something like an egg-stained plate with a jam-stained knife on the floor under a chair. This sometimes made me angry and silent with her. She feared my silences. One evening, when I had been perfectly quiet for fifteen minutes, she shouted 'Alright! If you really hate me so much why don't you hit me?'

'I never hit people!' said I indignantly, really shocked by the idea.

'But you want to! So do it! Do it!'

She rushed at me. I found myself shrinking back into a corner of the sofa, blushing and wriggling and giggling, 'I don't *want* to hit you!' as she frantically slapped and nipped me. One of her slaps struck my testicles, not hard enough to disable me because I grabbed her and spanked her and undressed her etcetera so it all ended tenderly with us both gloriously exhausted. Thereafter she brought most of my bad moods to that conclusion, but I had very few bad moods. She was messy and I was neat but she loved my neatness. We were making love one day when she started weeping, I hope tears of joy, and she cried out, 'Oh you're so neat and clean! So neat and clean!' She liked my clothes, especially the six identical trousers, and learned to iron and press them with great care. Perhaps she saw me as the sort of expensive doll she had longed for when she was wee.

*

I used to think Denny was foolish because she had no definite ideas about the world. I had very definite ideas: the world was a mess, but its problems could be solved by modern technology, and when Alan and I left college we would begin to improve things. I was an ignorant git. If intelligence asks searching questions and does not relax on a pile of glib answers Denny was the intelligent half of us. I once saw her frown and move her lips as if talking to herself. I touched her brow and said, 'What's happening in there?'

She said, 'Jock, what is the most important thing to know?'

'What do you mean?'

'I mean, my education was rubbish, the school taught me nothing. What should it have taught me?'

'It should have taught you to earn a decent wage.'

'No, I don't mean that, I think I mean geography. Surely geography is the most important thing?'

'Why?'

'Because if you don't know geography you don't know where you are, so everything you think is wrong. I used to think England was a different island from Scotland, like America is. Well, I know now it isn't a different island, but when I hear about all these other countries in the news, Korea and Berlin and Germany and Hungary, I don't know how far away they are so I don't know how much I should bother about them. Well-educated people stop me in the street with collecting cans, and they ask for money for the starving weans in Korea, and I give them a tanner if I have it because weans ought not to starve, that is definitely not right. And then I wonder, where is Korea? Won't it cost a lot of money to send my money to Korea? Would I do more good if I gave my tanner to my wee cousin in Shettleston who stays in a room where the floor is wet all the time?'

I could not answer these questions so I thought them naïve, but I can answer some of them now. I could tell Denny now, 'Geography no longer matters because there is no near or far, the monetary sheath enclosing the globe has destroyed the geography of distances. A company like Lonrho mines platinum in South Africa, insures lives in Bermuda, publishes half the Scottish newspapers and owns property everywhere. The Polish communist party crushes trade unions and keeps wages down to pay back money borrowed from the capitalist west. All the powers that be are in some sort of disreputable alliance, and they continue to be by allowing people like you, Denny, as little as possible in the way of knowledge and wages and living room. You were born in a trap, Denny, and will live and die in that trap, and if you bear a child the trap will pinch both of you harder and harder because the trap is getting fuller all the time. I was born in the long town, a trap for coal-miners. When the pit is shut down next year it will be a trap for the unemployed. My mother, by a skilful use of clothing and emotional blackmail, trapped me into doing my homework so as to free me from the long town and she succeeded. I became a free man who could choose his own job and I chose to work for the trap makers. Modern technology cannot solve the world's problems because in all societies technology is used to accumulate wealth, not spread it. The banking nations approve of revolts in the communist block, the communists want revolution in the capitalist block, but eastern communists grasp and increase their social privileges as much as our own Sunday-supplement-swallowing middle class who, if they ever notice you, Denny, will find your wish to understand the trap you are in amusingly naïve, quite charmingly pathetic and touching, really. But if you go on strike and demonstrate for better wages (you won't, you have no union, but if you do) then cabinet ministers drawing salaries of twenty-nine-thousand-nine-hundred-and-fifty-a-year (on top of interest on private investments) will appear on television to explain in brave, loud, haw-haw voices that there is not enough money to help you, that your selfish greed is the thing which has reduced Britain to its present deplorable plight. And if you are asked to say something in your own defence, Denny, your voice on the wireless waves will sound stupid and funny because you don't know how to address the public. Your school did not teach you to speak or think, it taught you to sit in rows and be quiet under strong teachers or rowdy under weak ones. The people who manage you, Denny, have been taught to make brazen speeches in firm clear voices, THAT is FAR more important than geography or technology, because RHETORIC RULES, OK?' (keep off politics). Thank you for reminding me, God. I will keep off politics.

I did not want to leave Denny all alone in that house. I asked her to come with me when I visited Alan, who admired her, but she said 'I'm never going to visit him.'

'Why not?'

'I hate that big Alan.'

'Why?'

'He thinks he can do anything he likes.'

She was right. In Alan's company I always felt that anything we imagined was possible. After a pause I said, 'That is no reason for hating him. He never wants to do nasty things.'

She said, 'Mibby he can do anything he likes but people like us cannae do anything we like.'

I saw then that Denny, who lacked proper parents and education and could not even dress properly, thought she and I were the same sort of person and Alan and I were not. This put me in a bad mood which I did not allow her to turn into a friendly sexy squabble. I became perfectly quiet and sat with my arms tightly folded on my knees and let her slap and nip me until she was exhausted and weeping and pleading; then I stood up and walked out of the house without saying a word.

It was a mild sunny summer evening so when Alan opened the door I suggested we go a walk and enjoy a pint somewhere. He was wearing pin-striped trousers tucked into wellington boots and a dirty collarless shirt with the sleeves rolled up. He said, 'Good idea, Jock, but let me finish this small job first.'

I followed him into the front room. He was stripping paint from a table he had found in a midden.

'A valuable antique?' I asked ironically, for it looked nothing special to me. He said, 'Not yet, but if I stain and polish and keep it for sixty-eight years it will become a valuable antique.'

The circular top was two feet across with a single, tapering leg ending in a tripod base. The tripod was certainly elegant. Alan showed me that the sections had been so dovetailed and angled that the joints would be strengthened, not weakened, by ordinary wear. He said, 'It won't last forever, of course. One day an unusually heavy weight will be placed off-centre on it here, and it will crack here.'

He touched a line in the grain of the wood. I said, 'Could you prolong its life by reinforcing that part?'

He said, 'No. It's too well made. Additional material would weaken the rest of the structure.'

He worked on the table for two hours, delicately scraping and sandpapering. I did not mind. We chatted, or I leafed through his piles of old technical magazines, or listened to the pigeons croodle-crooing in the chimney. At last he said, 'It's a bit late for a walk and a pint, Jock, and anyway I have no money. How much have you?'

I showed him a half-crown, a florin and sixpence. He said, 'My table has a Parisian look, let's have a continental evening at home. For less than that money you can buy a bottle of Old Tron, a unique full-blooded Scottish wine greatly favoured by the aficionados, the cognoscenti and connoisseurs. Use the change to purchase two cigars of the best quality. I will provide glasses, a match and, of course, the table.'

When I returned he had gained formal dignity by donning his army officer tunic and knotting a white cotton scarf round his throat. The newly cleaned table now stood before the open window and had three upright chairs round it and three glasses on top, besides a shining brass candlestick holding three inches of candle, and a clean saucer containing matches and a cigar cutter. Alan unwrapped the cigars and laid them across the saucer saying, 'It is not yet lighting-up time.'

He poured some of the red syrupy wine into two of the glasses, then carefully emptied the rest into a cut-glass decanter which he placed in the exact centre of the table. Like an experienced waiter he pulled out a chair and pushed it forward under my thighs as I settled into it, then sat opposite me. We touched glasses and sipped. I said, 'You are expecting more company.'

He said 'Avril may drop in.'

Avril was his girlfriend, an art student. He said, 'Why do you never bring Denny to see me?'

I told him what Denny had said. He sighed and said, 'She understands me. She really is very sharp. You ought to marry her.'

I said, 'I have just turned eighteen. Denny is the first and only woman I ever slept with, and she chose me, I did not choose her. And I will not marry till I earn a wage that will support two of us, without debt, in my own house.'

He said, 'Yes. A pity.'

I said, 'Will you marry Avril?'

'No no no. Have you seen how she handles her belongings? She likes books on art, she really does study the pictures and read the text, and because she is expertly shaped and exquisitely crafted plenty of infatuated dolts give her these books. And as soon as she owns one she gets it smeared with paint and bends the spine back till it cracks. She would treat me like that if I married her, so I never will. But I'm afraid we'll continue to see each other, probably even love each other, till death-do-us-part. Avril has a grip like an iron vice. I envy you with Denny.'

I said mildly, 'I don't believe a word of that.'

'A pity.'

The street was getting a ruddy tint from the descending sun. We watched it and sipped the wine, commenting on the passers-by and whatever we could see of life through the windows of the tenement opposite. Avril arrived, a slim girl with a lost lonely fascinating look. I think she was sorry to see me there but I don't know how she conveyed that. She was pleasant and friendly. She wore flat sandals, jeans, a paint-stained sweater and her hair in a pony tail. Alan said briskly, 'Avril, you are improperly dressed for a continental evening. Please go to the bedroom, take off all your clothes and put on this. And remove that rubber band from your hair, I am sure Parisiennes don't wear rubber in that particular place.'

He gave her a black dress which had belonged to his mother who must have been a big woman, for when Avril came from the bedroom it hung to her ankles and would not lie on both shoulders. She looked splendid. She could look splendid in any garment. Alan lifted her hair, laid the mass of it carefully on her naked shoulder, then placed behind her ear a convincing white blossom he had made a moment before by cutting and folding a sheet of paper. He handed her ceremonially to the chair between us and filled the three glasses with the last of the wine. The street lamps came on. He lit the candle, clipped the cigars and bade me set fire to mine first. For half an hour we sat sipping and smoking and watching the slow summer gloaming darken the street, and colour the sky above the opposite tenement, and bring electric lights on in the rooms facing us. I knew that the window framing this subtly altering picture was framing a picture for the street outside: a picture of a young candlelit woman seated between her lover, a fine tall man, and his friend, a refined smaller one. I felt, I'm sure we all felt, as good-looking, as interesting, as comfortable, as civilized, as everlasting, as contented as folk in a good painting by Renoir. Alan had contrived this, but the foundation of my contentment was the knowledge that Denny was waiting for me a mile to the west. My body was already anticipating the peaceful satisfaction she and I would know after we had delighted each other.

I returned later than I intended and was very glad to find Denny sitting in the kitchen chattering cheerfully to the landlord, who was appreciating her company. I had advised her to avoid him because I had feared he could not do that. He was a solemn young fledgling lawyer whom I greatly respected, perhaps because he was rather like me. He dressed in good suits, chose his words carefully and hardly ever smiled. But now he was chuckling. Denny was telling stories about her relations – the ones she disliked – and though the information shocked him he enjoyed being shocked and kept asking questions. She was exhilarated to find she could entertain a man of his sort. We all had a cup of tea together and when at last I said briskly, 'Bedtime, Denny,' he detained me for a moment as I was leaving the kitchen and whispered, 'You have a great wee woman there.'

When I embraced her that night I knew how very lucky I was. That was the happiest day of my life.

Alex. Hamilton

A sook fur freedom

ALEX. HAMILTON was born in Glasgow in 1949. He is a writer and reader of stories, and a composer and performer of songs. 'A sook fur freedom' is an extract from his novel *Stretch marks*, now complete and looking for a publisher.

'**S**o, you found it all right, then?'

Wullie was sitting fatly in one of the two easy chairs Liz had left in what she'd converted from her lounge to a temporary ballroom. His blue-encased thighs were spread apart, his back straight against the chair, and his arms stiff and jointed at the elbows along its rests. He held a can of McEwan's Lager in one hand and a half glass of red wine in the other, with his cigarette between fore- and middle-fingers of that fist which had to encircle the smaller diameter and did not, therefore, squash as much as the beer hand would have.

'Aw aye, nae boathir ataw. Ah wiz jiss sayin tae Liz, here,' Wullie nodded at her and smiled as she stood beside Frank with a comradely hand on his forearm, 'how Ah've goat pit oantae thi Byres Road depot noonagayn when thiv been a bit shoart a men. Telln yi, thriz nae quickir wey tae get tae know a narea thin emptyin folks' middins. Aw thi shoart-cuts, tae – mulliun za wee access lanes yid nivir iv knew wir therr fyi didnae hivtae . . .'

Frank let him talk on and ceased to listen. He was amazed at the man. Not because he looked so much at his ease in the foreign middle class environment, because Wullie was not a man to be overawed by surroundings – seen too much of the shite all foundations are built on for that, his whole attitude seemed to say. Nor because he looked so different in his Saturday mufti – scrubbed nails and shaven chops sat on him as comfortably as did the weekday grime: probably, Wullie felt it appropriate to the day of the week and, if it was appropriate, it would be uncomfortable to appear any other way. No. What amazed Frank was his speech: or, to be more exact, two aspects of it. The man was talking, actually conversing in a sociable, smiling way of which Frank had thought him incapable. When he spoke on the run, if he spoke on the run, it was either curt instruction or rounded curse which seemed to indicate that everything had been said before, that work was to be tholed for the wage packet it brought and that the best course was to get on with the job and save breath for extra-curricular activity.

And the rounded curses themselves?

His speech had been a model of schoolroom propriety since Frank's arrival.

'. . . sivinteen year, near inuff,' he heard the reply to a question from Liz, whose voice had broken into one of Wullie's short silences and wakened Frank from his reverie. 'Maistly thi same depot wherr me an Frank ur thi noo, bit accasionally yi get shiftit oot tae len a haun – lik whit Ah wiz telln yi aboot when thiv sent us uptae Byres Road, frinstince.'

'Is that where you got the snazzy suit and tie?' Frank laughed, dodging out the way of the brilliantly polished shoe Wullie aimed at him playfully. 'Out one of those posh middens up by the Esquire House?'

Wullie turned to Liz and winked. 'See that, ih? Fly soanso's jiss tryin tae may kuz swerr in front a you, so e is. Well,' he took a swig at his can and a draw at the cigarette, 'e'll no get *that* satisfactiun, Ah'm telln yi.'

Liz laughed, and patted Frank where she held his arm.

'Ah, don't let that worry you, Willie; I'm pretty used to it from Frank and the rest of our friends. In fact, I'm none too good at controlling my own tongue when it comes to the pinch. Fucking useless, as a matter of fact.'

Wullie looked quite offended.

'Aw,' he said, 'Ah see. Well,' he upended his glass, drained his can and dropped his cigarette butt into it, then swirled it round till he heard it swish itself out. Ah'll mine da that afore thi night soot, Ah derr say – thanks fur let nuz know. Eh, kin yi tell us wherr thi lavatri is, please?'

Liz released Frank's arm and took hold of Wullie's sleeve.

'Of course,' she smiled. 'It's just out here into the hall, and then the first door on the right. Come on and I'll show you – I want to go and put some make-up on anyway.'

Frank winked as they moved for the door, but Wullie merely looked bemused. He shook his head in slow reply and meekly allowed himself to be led away.

Nobody else had arrived and, as it was twenty minutes till closing time, Frank didn't expect to see anyone for another half-hour. He made his way into the kitchen and extracted a tin of Pale Ale from his carry-out before setting the bag beside the booze Liz had laid on

the table where the other guests would put their contributions when
they did come. He noticed with satisfaction that there was a half bottle
of Black Rum, and tied a knot in his mental handkerchief to remind
himself of it for later on. He didn't normally drink spirits, but five
or six tinned beers always left a vaguely metallic taste at the back
of his throat which a shot of rum relieved best. He had half thought
of getting a barrel of pressurized beer for the evening, but there hadn't
been enough time to organize the split: if you put yourself to any
expense before extracting more than promises from these bastards,
they swilled your drink and promptly forgot to pay. He was smilingly
aware of his hypocrisy as he poured half the rum into a mug and
sat it behind the vegetable rack which Liz kept in the cupboard under
the sink. It's a hard world, he thought. But when it belongs to some
poncer like Liz who's got so much money she doesn't have to work
during the holidays . . .

He took a swig at his can.

So, he thought, and surprised himself by shivering a little. To the
fray.

Wullie was standing with his back to the unlit gas fire when Frank
went back into the sitting room. Liz had put on an early Stones LP
and turned the treble right down so that Bill Wyman's predictable
but exciting bass line was thump-droning insistently up from the carpet
and fuzzing the ears. If the tone wasn't adjusted by the time he'd
had a few more beers, Frank knew he was going to have a hell of
a time trying to sort one thought from its neighbour, and translate
each into single, comprehensible items of speech.

Wullie waved him over.

'Dyou get your slash, then?'

'Aw aye, fun it nae boathir. An a gey nice cludge it is, tae. Fact,
it sa helluva nice fuckin place awthigithir, so it is. Diz shi sherr it
wi mate san that? Rent muss be fuckin skyhigh. Here.'

He shoved his packet of Capstan at Frank who raised his eyebrows
in mock wonder. 'Ta. Things looking up? Dyou have a win on the
dogs or something?'

'Naw, naw,' Wullie replied, striking a match and lighting the cigarettes. 'IvAh nivir telt yi it sa mug's gemm, thi bettin? Naw? FAh'm
gaw noot eniwherr speciul, Ah olwiz buy these – thir ma palite fag
zAh sippose, ma speciul wans, know whit Ah mean?'

Frank shrugged.

'Ah well, they're very nice – I remember you had them at that party *you* took *me* to. But I just always stick to the same thing. Can't afford to get a taste for luxury when you're a student.'

'Aye,' Wullie nodded, 'an no fyirra fuckin dussmin eethir, Ah'll tell yi. Bit lissn,' and he wagged the cigarette hand at Frank's nose to emphasize his point, 'this is thi diffrince bitween you an me – bitween *aw* youse,' his hand swept round the room including in its arc everyone who might arrive, 'an me – bitween aw youse an aw *us*: us bein me an Rab an Joe – aye, an evin fuckin Freddy inaw, cum tae that.'

'What? What difference?' Frank asked. 'What difference do you mean?'

'Well, jiss lookit *you*, frinstince; look how yir dresst.'

Frank cast an eye down and over his jeans, T-shirt and denim waistcoat. He shrugged.

'What do you mean, *how I'm dressed*? I don't see anything unusual about it – I'm just the same as I always am. You've never seen me looking any different.'

'Aye.' Wullie nodded, his eyes gleaming with argument. 'That's jiss tit, son. Ah nivir *hiv* saw yi look neni diffrint, yir dead right. Iz yi says a minute ago therr, yir jiss thi same iz yi olwiz ur. Wee bit cleanir thin yir wurkin claes, mibbe, bit stull jiss thi fuckin same.'

Frank swigged back the last of his beer, and grimaced at the aftertaste of metal where lees ought to have been.

'So?' he asked.

'*So*, son, whit yiv goat tae undirstonn is this,' Wullie went on. 'Noo, Ah doant gie a fuck aboot you makin snidey comments aboot ma Settirday suit. Ah doant mineji takin wana ma Settirday fag zan sayn yi couldnae afford thim yirsel: which means – really, fyi thing kabootit – thit yir criticizin me fur be nextravagint it thi weeken an then hivin tae cadge roll-up san moan aw week aboot no hivin nuthn left. Bit lissn,' he put a hand on Frank's shoulder and led them to the kitchen and the drinks table, 'aw that's nuthn. Jiss jokes. Bantir bitween wurkmate san so it means nuthn merr na *good mornin* ur a *up yours*. Passiz thi time. Jiss whit yi say tae wan anuthir. Here,' he stopped, pulled the bottle of El Dorado from a jacket pocket and almost smiled. 'Wir gettin too serious. Opin uzup a coupla can za lagir an get a sluga this doon yi.'

Frank reached for the tins of beer but demurred at the cheap wine.

'Lissn, ya cunt,' Wullie's near smile was there still, but his eyes were narrow with concentration, 'this is a good illastratiun a whit Ah'm tryn tae say tae yi. When sumbdi, sumbdi thit wid slay iz ain maw fur a gless durin thi week, offirs yi a go it thi bevvy e's wurk tiz gut soot fur, yi doant fuckin go *no thank you very much*. By jeeziz christ, yi fuckin doant! See fit wiz poxy piss ur strained fuckin fanny pads, yid get fuckin beltit intae it so yi wid, an thank god thir wiz sumbdi in thi wurld thit wantit tae say sumhin tae yi!'

He paused and looked away, searching the walls for calm and inspiration.

'It's jiss kiz sumbdi *hisnae goat thi wurds* thit yi should realize whit e's daein is speakin. Fur fucksake, Frankie, Ah thoat yi wir study nInglish upit that collidge – yi muss hiv sum kinna fuckin brains, bit whit yi hiv fuckin nane ae is a wee bit christianity, fur fucksake! A wee bit *undirstonnin*!'

Frank was glad he had the wine to gulp.

'Christ, Wullie,' he said, passing back the bottle and wiping a nervous and non-existent dribble off his chin. 'Christ, I'm sorry, pal. I never knew. I mean ... what I mean is ... I mean, you know? You know what I'm getting at? What I mean is ...'

'Whityi mean is, yi doant like thi wine.' Wullie clapped him on the shoulder and almost-smiled again. 'Sawright son, Ah know that, same wey izAh know thirz nae affence in yi. Bit whit yi mean an whit yi ur's two differint things sumtimes. Whit Ah mean is, whit *Ah* mean is whit *you* urnae – bit it sno ivribdi this wid be able tae folla that. Know whit Ah mean?'

'*Know what you mean?*' Frank laughed, threw an arm round Wullie's shoulder and led him to the small two-seater couch which Liz had stuck in a corner when she was creating her unencumbered dance area. 'Christ Wullie, you're as clear as some of the lecturers up the road there. Which is to say: *as fuckin mud!* Come on and we'll have a seat and you can explain what you mean. I mean – no insult intended, or that – you seem to know what *you* mean *and* what *I* mean, and I want enlightened. I mean, if I knew just the one of them, I'd think I was fuckin lucky!'

He stopped and faced Wullie just as they turned to sit down. 'I'm serious,' he said in quiet contradiction to the late hysteria of his tone and manner. 'And, believe me, I'm getting at nobody – except maybe myself.'

Wullie sighed and lowered his bulk onto the couch.

'Ah know, Frank, Ah know. Yirra decint cunt, nAh'm no sayn yi urnae. Niza mattirafact, Ah widnae evin boathir tae talk tae yi fAh didnae think yi wirnae – Ah widiv goat yi kick taff thi squad eftir thi furss day, an yida been push na brush aboot Temple fur thi hale a yir hoaliday zan bring nin evin less pennies thin yi ur noo.'

'I know,' Frank nodded, and produced his tin. 'I do my best. Want a roll?'

'Heh!'

Wullie leant forward and slapped his knee. A childlike enthusiasm rushed over his face and gave him a look of cherubic relief.

'Ah've goatit! Ah know how Ah kin ixplain it tae yi – bit yill need tae promise us wan thing, awright?'

Frank nodded, smiling.

'Well, yir no tae interrupt us. Yiv tae say nuthn tull Ah'm by kiz, if yi dae, Ah'm liable tae get ma train a thought intirruptit an firget whit it wiz Ah wiz gonnae say. Ah'm no used wi wurds, nenihin merrn hauf a duzzin thigithir's merrn likely tae jiss taboot sweat thi fuckin gut sootae us.'

Frank started a shrug of encouraging denial, but Wullie put out a hand to forestall his opening his mouth to speak.

'Naw. Say nuthn. Youse guys used wi wurds kin ferr unsettle a nordinri mortil when e's tryin tae ixpress izsel. Fyi agree no tae intarrupt us, jiss start thi noo bae no sayn nuthn. Nod yir heid an let us get oan wi it. Gaun – noddit fyi agree.'

Frank smiled; and nodded.

Wullie did smile now.

'Yi agree, well?'

Frank nodded again and Wullie let out a sigh which was a mixture of relief, and of trepidation at having committed himself.

'Christ,' he said. 'Ah doant know whit Ah've let masel in fur, neer Ah dae. Bettir hiv a fag tae get startit.'

He lit one, took a long pull at the neck of his wine bottle, and placed it on the carpet between them.

'Fyi want a dring kafore Ah'm finisht yill need tae tay ka guzzil it that, ya cunt: yiv nae beer lef tan yir gaun fuckin *no*where tull Ah've goat aw ma wurd zoot.'

He took a deep drag at his Capstan, blew a lungful of smoke at the lit end and watched it kindle brighter for a long moment before he went on.

'It wiz this fag thit gie duz thi idea,' he began. 'Ur tae be merr ixact, it wiz that fag thit *you* offir dus. See, it pit us in mine da this filim Ah seen wance – aw, fuckin year zago it muss be noo – wi yon dame wi thi shuge knockir zinit. Jane Sumhin – brunette – Yank, a course – christ, whitsit agayn? – naw, you shut yir fuckin face you, an mine whit Ah tellt yi aboot no speakin! It soan thi tippa ma – Russell! That sit! an Ah widnae a mindit gettin fuckin terrier dintae ur wi thi tippa ma prick, Ah'll tell yi! Naw, doant even laugh, ya cunt! Ah might think yir laugh nit me an no ma joke, an that wid pit us aff fur ivir – an loass you a moothfae a teeth inaw!

'Eniwey, Jane Russell in this filim. Shiz this ex-con, right, an thi day shiz get noota thi prisin shi hiztae go an see thi chaplin ur sociul wurkir ur sumbdi thit's gie dur a joab ur sumhin. Ah cannae jiss mine daw thi details, bit it sno importint. Less jiss say it's sumbdi in athoriti, and shiz gettin ur wee pep talk afore shi go zoot intae thi big, bad wuril dagayn. So a course in these situatiuns – whit Ah mean is like when Ah wizin thi Army an cumin back intae civvy street: Ah've nivir been inside, thank fuck. In these kinna situatiuns, enihow, yi olwiz get pitit yir ease an thi sumbdi in athoriti gies yi a cuppa tea an a fag ur it leass says yi hiv pirmissiun tae smoke. So. Therr's Titsy Russell, well. Get noot, in furur wee talk, and tellt shiz tae may kursel it hame.

'Suddinli, but, yir aware ae a kinna silence, an that's kiz this sociul wurkir wummin's stoap tur wee bit sermin kiz shiz saw sumhin shi diznae like. Ah mean, wi doant know whit it is, bit wi defnitli know sumhin zup kiz thi face get saw prim dup an Jane, a course, realizes sumhin's wrang inaw kiz thi dame's cut ursel aff. So, shi stoaps whit shiz daein an look sorr it ur alminir pal.

'Camra, noo. Shoot sacroass tae thi chaplin's face an yi see thi eyes gettin cass doon; shoots back tae Jane an yi see *hur* eyes foallayin thi uthir wan's; back tae thi goody an shiz goat focus tin oan sumhin defnit; so right back tae thi Terrier an yi get thi camra gaun doon, doon, dead slow fae ur eyes, tae ur neck, tae ur tits – nAh'll fuckin swerr it hung about therr fur a helluva loat longir nit hid tae an certinli fur a helluva loat longir nit spent oan thi uthir bit sae ur – an doon agayn an then lassly it settle zoan ur lap wherr shiz fiddlin aboot wi a coupla strand za cheap shag ana cigarette paypir izif shiz fondlin sum lucky cunt's limp, wee prick.

' "Naw," goes thi alminir, "doant dae that, hen."

' "Doant dae whit, Yir Majisti?" Jane asks back.

' "Rollups, hen," she says. "Fyi get intae a nice wee joab an spin thim yir yar naboot hivin been wurk nin Bostin ur sumwherr aw thi time yiv been inside, yi might jiss get away wi it fyir cinsistint anuff an doant may keni daf blundirz. Bit," shi go zoan, "see fyi bring oot yir hauf ounce a" – Bull Durham, Ah thing kit wiz – "see fit coffee time yi bring oot yir hauf ounce a Bull Durham? That's you brandit, hen. Yir covir story's shot tae fuck kiz naebdi, nae *wummin*, that is, haunroll zur cigarette sinless shiz been sumwherr wherr that's thi oanlie kinna smoke yi kin get yir haun zoan."

' "Aw," goes Jane, slow-drawl like, an yi kin see thi truth a this dawnin slow oan ur face inaw. "Ah see whit yi mean." An up shi gets, walk sorr tae thi desk, an throw zaw ur fuckin aquipment intae thi wastepapir baskit.

' "Awright?" shi asks, brushin thi strand za tabacca affur fanny wi they big man-grabbin haunza hurs. "Howzat? Ah've swep these past five years right oota ma life" ur sum crappy fuckin line lik that, an thi sociul wurkir, aw palsy-walsy an that, kinna pat sur oan thi heid an gie zur a packit a tailir-mades fur bein such a good wee lassie.

'Right. Enda story, bit doant opin yir mooth yit, ya cunt. Ah've oanlie jiss fuckin startit.'

Wullie grabbed his bottle from the floor, took a good swig at it and held it out to Frank with eyebrows raised in an insistent interrogative. The younger man nodded, swallowed down a big, sticky gulp without grueing, and passed it back.

Wullie smiled.

'Good fur you, son. Yiv learnt *sum*hin.'

He had a second, smaller drink then placed the bottle back on the floor between them.

'Yi get use tae it, ih – thi nice, warmy wey it hits yir guts? Mibbe nix time yill no hivtae be askt.'

Frank could see from the delicate glaze on Wullie's eyes that that nice warmth was beginning to spread a bit further than Wullie's gut. He wondered if this was the first bottle he'd consumed that day.

'Heh son,' Wullie went on, sitting back into the couch again. 'Ur you feelin awright? Mine jir no tae answir, noo! Yir eye ziv goat a kinna veil drew orr thim lik wana they muslin things thi beekeepirz pit oan when thir movin hives.'

He paused a moment to look, glassy but straight, at Frank then, and Frank would never have believed a report of it, he giggled.

'Mine joo, son,' he got out after struggling successfully for control of himself, 'mibbe it sno *your* eyes thit saw glaze dowir – mibbe it's mines thit's makin thim *look* that wey!'

Frank acknowledged what he felt: shame. If he'd even vaguely entertained such a self-criticism of his capacity for drink, he'd certainly never have mooted it publicly; and probably not even to himself.

'Eniwey,' Wullie gave himself a vigorous, verbal shake. 'That saw baeside thi point, intit? Wiv goat tae get oan wi wir story noo thit Ah've went this faur. Snae good me telln you a wee memary ae a filim fit's no gaun eniwherr, izit? Ah mean, Ah might jiss tiz well iv went oan aboot thi lass tepasode a "Coranatiun Street" if tell na

story zaw it saboot? Naw. It sno a story Ah'm tryin tae tell yi, Frankie
– bit whit Ah'm ur tryin tae dae is – is whit? Spin yi a yarn? Ih?
Aye, heh that's good, intit? True inaw, tae. *Spin yi a fuckin yarn.*

'An here's how. It leass, here's how sumhin yi done pit us in mine
da thi story a that filim, an here's how Me-Big-Knockirz-Jane pit us
in mine da *you* – wi nae disraspect tae thi wummin intendit!

'See fAh kin pitit ina coupla wurds.

'Jane smokes roll-ups: you smoke roll-ups.

'Jane zup agaynss tit: you rup agaynss fuckaw!'

He advanced one hand to the bottle and held the other palm in
an imperious halt before Frank could begin to speak.

'Naw,' he said after he'd taken a swig and caught a line of sweat
on a forefinger as it formed above his eyebrow. 'Yiv been dead patient
son, so jiss gie zanuthir coupla minnits. Ah'm nearly therr noo.'

He placed the bottle between them once more and lit himself a
cigarette absentmindedly without offering the packet to Frank.

'Aye,' he went on, exhaling relief with his cloud of smoke, 'jiss
taboot therr noo, son.' He grinned. 'See fyi kin let us getit oot afore
yi belt us wan – though it sno *you* Ah'm tryin tae insult. Fact, Ah'm
no tryin tae insult naebdi ataw. Merr lik jiss tryin tae ixplain
sumhin – a nattitude a mind.

'See, Jane Russell in that filim wiz gaw noot intae thi big, bad wuril
deftir spendin so minny year zinside fur bein a nenimy a saciety an
that. Shid get oota therr wi a coupla dollir zin ur purse an, it thi
very bess, sum kinna shitey joab thit a nimployir wi a consciunce – ur
a neye fur cheap labour, merrn likely – hiz gie dur tae try an get
ur rispectible and back oan thi right track sagayn. Noo, that lassie's
gonnae hiv wan helluva hard time makin enz meet oan whitivir skitteri,
wee wages shi get san, if shi diz smoke, yid think shid go ootae ur
wey tae kee poan buyin thi cheapiss wanz so's shi kin spend whitivir
sperr cash shi hiz goat oan a wintir coat, shoes, may-kup ur a coupla
steel reinforced fuckin brassieres tae keep they magnificent tit sa hurs
in sum kinna ordir. Bit diz shi? Diz shi fuck. An how? Kiz wance
it's been pointit ootae ur jiss whit rollin yir ain means tae folk watch
na wummin, it autamaticlli's gonnae mean thi same tae hur fur ivir
eftir. Ivri drag a ivri fag that wummin smokes, son, is a sook fur
freedom. A rimindir thit whit shiz daein shiz daein noo iza free
wummin, oota clink an celabratin; aye, fuckin *celabratin*'s thi wurd
fur it – celabratin ur liberti bae consciously rifusin tae buy cheap fuckin
shag jiss tae gie intae a cravin. Whit shiz daein's merrn jiss satisfy na
need fur tabacca: shiz satisfy na nurge tae turn roon tae thi wurild,

blaw smoke in its wee rid eye zin say tae it: "Up yours, pal! Ah've
ivri right tae enjoy masel iz much iz youse hiv, nif Ah want a smoke,
naebdi's gonnae turn roon an say *therr za fuckin jailbird*, jiss kizAh
hivnae inuff cash tae buy a packit a fuckin readies!"

'Christ son, ji see whit Ah moan aboot? Awright, it's show fyi like,
an mibbe undir that heavin jumpir a hurs shiz werr na durti aul bra
when whit shi save zina month oan fags wid buy ur a spankin, new,
fuckin Clyde-built luxury wan. Mibbe shiz goat aul holey knickir zoan
fur thi same reasin, an mibbe they may kur fanny uncomfurtible when
shi crossiz ur legs tae keep pry neye zoot ur cunt oan thi subway.
Bit wan ae thi reasins they pryin eye ziz tryin tae get up ur crack
is kiz shiz spent whitivir coupla bob shiz goat oan a new skirt ur
a blouse ur sumhin yi fuckin *see* – kiz whit wid be merr uncomfurtible
thin a draughty vagina wid be sumbdi look nit yi an sayn tae thirsels,
"Aye, aye. Here za paupir", ur "Here sum cunt jiss toota thi nick
an stull in its demob suit", ur – an here whit Ah'm *really* oan aboot –
"Here a fuckin dussman, intit? Yi kin tell bae thi dungarees an thi
denim jaikit an thi shurt thit's twó sizes too big – ur too wee – kiz
e diznae earn anuff tae buy izsel decint claes *an* hiv a pint a beer an
a gill a thi wine inaw. An roll-ups, that sa dead giveaway, tae. Thi fancy
suit, thi natty tie, thi poalisht shoes – an then it saw ruined when e go
zintae iz Italian-cut poackit an bring zoot thi aul basht Goldin Virginia
tin an starts roll nizsel a smoke.

'Son,' Wullie clapped one hand on Frank's knee, braced the other
on an arm of the couch and pushed himself to his feet. 'Son, yi kin
olwiz tell who's wurkin class when yir oot eniwherr: the men wi thi
suit san thi wummin wi thi herr-does. Thi wans thit loo kizif thiv
jiss goat oot thir bed zeftir sleep nin thir denim zan polo-necks, ur
firgoat tae pit oan thir may-kup eftir gaun straight oot fur a bevvy
eftir thi backshift – these ur yir lawyir zan yir teachir zan yir bank
wurkirs. Thi weeken za hoaliday, son, an a hoaliday za cheinge, a
fuckin topsy-turvy cheinge in ivri fuckin wey: wurk tae nae-wurk –
sober tae drunk *an* smart tae scruff an scruff tae smart fur ivri bastirt.
Sept fur youse fuckin studints, a course. Bit then, youse ur jiss tinjoyin
yirsels fur three ur four years, intyiz? Ah mean, denim zan polo-necks
while yiz kin, kiz soon yizur gonnae be earnin that much munni yizull
no be able tae *afford* tae go aboot lik fuckin tramp sur midgie men.
Ah'm away fur a slash.'

Tony Harrison

Six Poems

TONY HARRISON was born in Leeds in 1937. He has published several books of poetry including *The Loiners* which won the Geoffrey Faber Memorial Prize in 1972 and most recently *Continuous* (Rex Collings, 1981). He has written much dramatic verse in the form of libretti for the Metropolitan Opera, New York, and for collaborations with several leading modern composers, and verse texts for the National Theatre including *The Misanthrope* (1973), *Phaedra Britannica* (1975), *The Passion* (1977) and most recently *The Oresteia* (1981) which was also performed in the ancient theatre of Epidaurus, and was awarded the European Poetry Translation Prize in 1983. His *Selected Poems* will be published by Penguin in 1984.

Facing North

'The North begins inside.'
Louis MacNeice

*G*od knows why of all rooms I'd to choose
    the dark one facing North for me to write,
    liking as I do air, light and views,
though there's air in the North Wind that rocks the light
I have to keep on, all year round, all day;
nor why, despite a climate I profess to hate,
and years spent overseas, I stay,
and, when I start to pack, procrastinate.

The North Wind's part of it and when it blows
my shutters rattle and the front door slams
like memory shutting out half what it knows.
Here I poured huge passion into aerogrammes,
the lightest paper loaded with new hope
that made the old pain seem, on looking back,
seen through the wrong end of the telescope
making it so small I soon lost track.

The window's open to the winter's chill,
to air, to breezes and strong gusts that blow
my paper lantern nothing will keep still
and let me make things happen in its O.
When the circle, where my hand moves over white
with red and green advances on black ink,
first swung like this it gave me such a fright
I felt I was on a ship about to sink.

Now years of struggle make me concentrate
when it throws up images of planets hurled,
still glowing, off their courses, and a state
where there's no gravity to hold the world.
I have to hold on when I think such things
and weather out these feelings so that when
the wind drops and the light no longer swings
I can focus on an Earth that still has men,

in this flooded orchestra where elbow grease,
deep thought, long practice and much sweat
gave me some inkling of an inner peace
I'd never found with women till I met
the one I wrote all those air letters for
and she's the one I'm needing as I see
the North Wind once more strip my sycamore
and whip the last leaves off my elder tree.

Now when the wind flays my wild garden of its green
and blows, whistling through the flues, its old reminder
of the two cold poles all places are between,
though where she lives the climate's a lot kinder,
and starts the lightbulb swinging to and fro,
and keeps it swinging, switched off, back and forth,
I feel the writing room I'm leaving grow
dark, and then darker with the whole view North.

Flood

His home address was inked inside his cap
and on every piece of paper that he carried
even across the church porch of the snap
that showed him with mi mam just minutes married.

But if ah'm found at 'ome (he meant found dead)
turn t'water off. Through his last years he nursed,
more than a fear of dying, a deep dread
of his last bath running over, or a burst.

Each night towards the end he'd pull the flush
then wash, then in pyjamas, rain or snow,
go outside, kneel down in the yard, and push
the stop-cock as far off as it would go.

For though hoping that he'd drop off in his sleep
he was most afraid, I think, of not being 'found'
there in their house, his ark, on firm Leeds ground
but somewhere that kept moving, cold, dark, deep.

The Birds of America: Weeki Wachee

Duds doomed to join the dodo: the dugong,
talonless eagles, croc, gimp manatee,
here, courtesy Creation's generous strong,
the losers of thinned jungle and slicked sea.

Many's the proud chieftain used to strut
round shady clearings in dark festooned teak
with twenty cockatoo tails on his nut,
macaw plumes à la mode, rainforest chic.

Such gladrag gaudies safe in quarantine
and spared at least their former jungle fate
of being blowpiped for vain primitives to preen
now race a tightrope on one roller skate.

A tanned sophomore, these ghettoed birds' Svengali,
shows glad teeth, evolved for smiling, as macaws
perform their deft Darwinian finale
by hoisting the Stars and Stripes for our applause.

Cypress & Cedar

A smell comes off my pencil as I write
in the margins of a sacred Sanskrit text.
By just sufficient candlelight I skim
these scriptures sceptically from hymn to hymn.
The bits I read aloud to you I've Xed
for the little clues they offer to life's light.

I sit in mine, and you sit in your chair.
A sweetness hangs round yours; a foul smell mine.
Though the house still has no windows and no doors
and the tin roof's roughly propped with 4 × 4s
that any gale could jolt, our chairs are fine
and both scents battle for the same night air.

Near Chiefland just off US 129,
from the clapboard abattoir about a mile,
the local sawyer Bob displays his wares:
porch swings, picnic tables, lounging chairs,
rough sawn and nailed together 'cracker' style.
The hand I shake leaves powerful smells on mine.

Beside two piles of shavings, white and red,
one fragrant as a perfume, and one rank
and malodorous from its swampland ooze,
Bob displayed that week's work's chairs for me to choose.
I chose one that was sweet, and one that stank,
and thought about the sweet wood for a bed.

To quote the carpenter he 'stinks o' shite'
and his wife won't sleep with him on cypress days,
but after a day of cedar, so he said,
she comes back eagerly into his bed,
and, as long as he works cedar, there she stays.
Sometimes he scorns the red wood and works white!

Today I've laboured with my hands for hours
sawing fenceposts up for winter; one tough knot
jolted the chainsaw at my face and sprayed
a beetroot cedar dust off the bucked blade,
along with damp earth with its smell of rot,
hurtling beetles, termites in shocked showers.

To get one gatepost free I had to tug
for half an hour, but dragged up from its hole
it smelled, down even to the last four feet
rammed in the ground, still beautifully sweet
as if the grave had given life parole
and left the sour earth perfumed where I'd dug.

Bob gave me a cedar buckle for my belt,
and after the whole day cutting, stacking wood,
damp denim, genitals, 'genuine hide leather'
all these fragrances were bound together
by cedar, and together they smelled good.
It was wonderful the way my trousers smelled.

I can't help but suppose flesh-famished Phèdre
would have swept that prissy, epicene,
big-game hunting stepson Hippolyte,
led by his nose to cedar, off his feet,
and left no play at all for poor Racine,
if she'd soaped her breasts with *Bois de Cèdre*.

If in doubt ask Bob the sawyer's wife!
Pet lovers who can't stand the stink of cat
buy sacks of litter that's been 'cedarized'
and from ancient times the odour's been much prized.
Though not a Pharaoh I too favour that
for freighting my rank remains out of this life.

Why not two cedar chairs? Why go and buy
a reeking cypress chair as a reminder,
as if one's needed, of primeval ooze,
like swamps near Suwannee backroads, or bayous,
stagnation Mother Nature left behind her
hauling Mankind up from mononuclei?

Cypress still has roots in that old stew
paddling its origins in protozoa,
the stew where consciousness that writes and reads
grew its first squat tail from slimy seeds.
I'd've used it for the Ark if I'd been Noah,
though cedar, I know you'll say, would also do.

This place not in the *Blue Guide* or in *Fodor*
between the Suwannee River and the Styx
named by some homesick English classicist
who loved such puns, loathed swamps, and, lonely, pissed
his livelihood away with redneck hicks
and never once enjoyed the cedar's odour,

or put its smoke to snake-deterrent use
prescribed by Virgil in his *Georgics* III
with *chelydrus* here in the US South
construed as the diamondback or cottonmouth
which freed him, some said, from his misery.
Others said liquor, and others still a noose.

And, evenings, he, who'd been an avid reader
of the *Odyssey* and *Iliad* in Greek,
became an even avider verandah drinker
believing sourmash made a Stoic thinker
though stuck with no paddle up Phlegethon's creek,
and had no wife with a clothes chest of sweet cedar.

But you bought one at Bob's place and you keep
your cotton frocks in it, your underwear,
and such a fragrance comes from your doffed bras
as come from uncorked phials in hot bazaars,
and when you take your clothes off and lie bare
your body breathes out cedar while you sleep.

That lonely English exile named the river,
though it could have been someone like me, for whom,
though most evenings on the porch I read and write,
there's often such uneasiness in night
it creates despair in me, or drinker's gloom
that could send later twinges through the liver.

Tonight so far's been peaceful with no lightning.
The pecan trees and hophornbeams are still.
The storm's held off, the candleflame's quite straight,
the fire and wick united in one fate.
Though this quietness that can, one moment, fill
the heart with peace, can, the next, be frightening –

A hog gets gelded with a gruesome squeal
that skids across the quietness of night
to where we're sitting on our dodgy porch.
I reach for Seth Tooke's shotgun and the torch
then realize its 'farmwork' so alright
but my flesh also flinches from the steel.

Peace like a lily pad on swamps of pain –
floating's its only way of being linked.
This consciousness of ours that reads and writes
drifts on a darkness deeper than the night's.
Above that blackness, buoyed on the extinct,
peace, pure-white, floats flowering in the brain,

and fades, as finally the nenuphar
we found on a pewter swamp where two roads ended
was also bound to fade. The head and heart
are neither of them too much good apart
and peace comes in the moments that they're blended
as cypress and cedar at this moment are.

My love, as prone as I am to despair,
I think the world of night's best born in pairs,
one half we'll call the female, one the male,
though neither essence need, in love, prevail.
We sit here in distinctly scented chairs
you, love, in the cedar, me the cypress chair.

Though tomorrow night I might well sit in yours
and you in mine, the blended scent's the same
since I pushed my chair close to your chair
and we read by the one calm candle that we share
in this wilderness that might take years to tame,
this house still with no windows and no doors.

Let the candle cliché come out of the chill –
'the flickering candle on a vast dark plain'
of one lone voice against the state machine,
or Mimi's on cold stairs aren't what I mean
but moments like this now when heart and brain
seem one sole flame that's bright and straight and still.

If it's in Levy County that I die
(though fearing I'd feel homesick as I died
I'd sooner croak in Yorkshire if I could)
I'll have my coffin made of cedar wood
to balance the smell like cypress from inside
and hope the smoke of both blends in the sky,

as both scents from our porch chairs do tonight.
'Tvashti', says this Indian Rig Veda,
'hewed the world out of one tree', but doesn't tell,
since for durability both do as well,
if the world he made was cypress wood; or cedar
the smell coming off my pencil as I write.

Aqua Mortis

Death's elixirs have their own golden gleam.
I see you clearly: one good, failing eye's
on morning piss caught clumsily 'midstream'
it's your first task of the day to analyse.

Each day dawns closer to the last *eureka*,
the urine phial held up to clouding rays
meaning all solutions in life's beaker
precipitate one night from all our days.

Alchemists keep skulls, and you have one
that stretches your skin taut and moulds your face,
and instead of a star sphere for sense of space
there's the transatlantic number of your son,
a 14-digit spell propped by the phone
whose girdling's giddy speed knocks spots off Puck's
but can't re-eye dry sockets or flesh bone.

My study is your skull. *I'll burn my books.*

The Lords of Life

The snake our cracker neighbour had to scotch
was black and white and beautiful to watch.
I'd watched it shift its length, stay still, sashay,
shunting its flesh on shuffled vertebrae
for days before, and thought of it as 'mine'
so long had I wondered at its pliant spine.
My neighbour thinks it queer my sense of loss.
He took a branch festooned with Spanish moss,
at the cooler end of one hot afternoon,
and pestled my oaksnake's head into a spoon
he flourished laughing at his dogs, then slung
the slack ladle of its life to where it hung
snagged on a branch for buzzards till, stripped bare,
it trailed like a Chinese kite-string in the air.
Waal! he exclaimed, *if ahda knowed you guys*
liked *snakes on your land* ... he turns and sighs
at such greenhornery. I'd half a mind
to say I'd checked the snake's a harmless kind
in *two* encyclopaedias but knew the looks
I'd get from him for 'talking books.' —
There's something fairy (I can hear him say)
about a guy that watches *snakes all goddam day!*
The wife he bullies says: *O Bill, let be!*
There's doers and there's watchers, maybe he ...
Ain't no doer, says he, *that's plain to see!*
I seed him sit out on their porch and read
some goddam great Encyclopaed-
ia, yeah, read! *What does the fairy DO?*
O Bill! she says, *not everyone's like you.*
And you'd be the first man to stand up and say
that people living in the USA
have every right to live the way they please. —
Yeah! But those guys look too young for retirees!
Nothing that I did made any sense
but I think he offered me as recompense
for battering my snake the chance to see
the alligators on his property.

Each Sunday his riding mower wouldn't stop

till every blade of grass had had its crop,
so that the bald, burned earth showed through the green
but any snake that trespassed was soon seen.
That was the front, but out there in the back
he hadn't even hacked a proper track
down to the swampy lake, his own retreat
kept wild as the front part was kept neat.
This was his wilderness, his very own
left just as it was, rank, overgrown,
and into this he went with guns and beer
to wallow in his dreams of the frontier
and shot the gators we were seeing glide
with egrets on their backs from side to side.
The egrets ride in threes their gator skiffs,
Pharaoh's sarcophagi with hieroglyphs!
He offered me his rifle: *Wanna try?*
Go for the big ones not the smaller fry!
They've taken gators off the Endangered List.
I took aim and, deliberately, missed.
He blasted three egrets like a fairground shy
and then the gator they were ferried by.
Then we sat down at his fire and watched the day,
now reddened at the edges, drain away.
This hissing of damp logs and ringpull *Bud*
drunk from the can, his seal of brotherhood
(the sort where I'd play Abel and him Cain!)
I can't stand his beer but don't complain
as he flings them across the fire for me to catch:
round 1: the shooting, 2: the boozing match!
Each dead can he crushed flat and tossed aside
(When I was safe back home I also tried
and found, to my great chagrin, aluminum
crushable with pressure from one thumb!)
We stare into his cookout and exchange
neighbourly nothings, gators still in range.
Liberal with his beer-cans he provokes
his gator-watching guest with racist jokes.
Did you know, sir, that gators only eat
dogs and niggers, darker sortsa meat?
But you can eat him if he won't eat you.
I'll give you a gator steak to barbecue.

(He knew that cooking's something that I *do!*)
He'd watched me cooking, and, done out of doors,
cooking could be classed among male chores.
His suspicions of me as some city loafer
who couldn't gut a mullet or stew gopher
I tried, when I felt him watching, to dispel
by letting him see me working, working well.
I make sure, when he stares over, my swing's true
when I heave the axe like I've seen rednecks do,
both hands well-balanced on the slippery haft,
or make certain that he sees me when I waft
the coals to a fierce glow with my straw hat,
the grill bars spitting goat or gator fat.
If them fireants ain't stopped with gasoline
you can say goodbye to every inch of green.
They say on the TV they'll eat their way,
if we don't check 'em, through the USA!
The 'red peril's' what we call them bugs down here.
(A hiss for those villains from his seventh beer!)
From this house, you know, we're near enough to see
space launchings live. The wife watched on TV,
then dashed outside, and saw, with her own eyes,
'like a silver pen', she said, 'The Enterprise',
then rushed back for the message from the Prez
who'd just been wounded by some nut. He says:
We feel like giants again! Taking over space
has made Goliaths of the human race.
Me, I was in the rowboat, trying to relax.
I'd gotten me some chicken, 2 or 3 6-packs
like relaxing, and I zoomed out of a snooze
with a sudden start, the way you do with booze,
and saw our spaceship, clear as I see you,
like a bullet disappearing in the blue.
I must say that it made me mighty proud.
I sang God Bless America *out loud*
to those goddam alligators then I got
the biggest of the brutes with one sharp shot.
(But a man might get, say, lovesick, then he shoots
not one of your unendangered gator brutes
that glide so gracefully through silver ooze
and gladden gourmets in those Cross Creek stews,

and instead of potting dumb beasts like your gators
shoots the most acknowledged of all legislators,
on whose scaled back as corpse and cortège glide
the egret of the soul bums its last ride!)

Stuck goat fat's spitting from my still hot grill.
I've eaten very well, and drunk my fill,
and sip my *Early Times,* and to and fro
rock in the rocker watching ashes blow
off the white-haired charcoals and away
into the darkness of the USA.
Higher than the fireflies, not as high as stars,
the sparks fly up between the red hot bars.
I want no truck myself with outer space
except to gaze on from some earthly place
very much like this one in the South,
the taste of *Early Times* warm in my mouth.
Popping meals in pills in zero G
's not the dining that would do for me.
I'm feeling too composed to break the spell
when mosquitoes probe the veins of mine that swell
like blue earthworms. A head with sting
burrows in the blue, starts syphoning.
Let be! the watcher in me says, *Let be!*
but suddenly the doer side of me
(though my cracker neighbour couldn't, though he'd tried,
fathom if I'd got a doer side!)
swats the bastard and its legs like hair
sprout from my drop of blood on the cane chair.
The day's heat rolls away to make night thunder.
I look at the clouded planets and I wonder
if the God who blessed America's keen eye,
when He looked on that launching, chanced to spy,
in this shrinking world with far too many men,
either the cock-pecked wife who saw a pen . . .

(If I'd seen it going I'd've said
it was my snake sprayed silver, whose black head
my neighbour battered concave like a spoon,
pointing its harmless nose towards the moon,
lacquered in rigor mortis and not bent

into eternity's encirclement,
curled in a circle, sucking its own tail,
the formed continuum of female/male,
time that devours and endlessly renews,
time the open maw and what it chews,
the way my snake got chewed down here on earth,
the emblem of continuous rebirth
a bleached spine like one strand of Spanish moss –
for all the above *vide sub* Ouroboros!
All this is booktalk, buddy, mere Encyclopaedia know-how, not for *men*!) . . .

either the cock-pecked wife who saw a pen,
or the lurching rowboat where a red-faced man's
sprawled beside his shotgun and crushed cans,
who saw a bullet streak off on its trek,
and to that watching God was a mere speck,
the human mite, his rowboat lapped with blood,
the giant gator hunter killing BUD!

David Harsent

The Giant Christ
on the Road
to Marsalforn

DAVID HARSENT was born in Devonshire in 1942. He has published several volumes of verse, the most recent of which – *Dreams of the Dead* (O U P) – won the Geoffrey Faber Memorial Prize. A new collection, *The Punch Poems*, is in preparation, as is the continuum of stories which includes 'The Giant Christ on the Road to Marsalforn'.

1

At Xlendi she extended her hand, palm-up, her elbow a pivot on the side of the cane-bound chair. His own hand didn't move. Undeceived, he knew that she was putting the sun to the white skin on the underside. There was a seam in the sea where a deep blue met the harbour's aquamarine. He sat with her outside the St Patrick's Hotel, coffee untouched, watching the bright boats rise and slide on the swell. He lodged his forearms on his own chair so that the shadow-pattern of their fingers interlaced. She was unaware of that tiny violation; even so, she moved her position and sighed.

'Do you want to move on for lunch?'

She didn't reply so he said her name. She jerked like someone coming awake and swerved in the chair, her arm circling in a fluent motion to collect her coffee cup. Raising it to her lips, she sipped, and asked what he'd said. 'I was dozing,' she explained.

'Shall we move on somewhere for lunch?'

'You like it here, don't you?'

'I do. I thought perhaps . . .'

'Yes, why not. Pay the bill, then.'

She got up and walked very slowly to the low wall where the sea stopped. She was thinking of something. There was almost no noise: the foam lipping the sand, a fan ticking when he went into the hotel to settle up. No bird-song, no undertone of insects. Each day, she loafed through the midday scorch; he survived it at her side, shining with cream under the Panama, looking for cafés where he could order a coffee to have the water that came with it. Like a man flirting with a confession or rehearsing the public pronouncement of a private decision, almost speaking, welcoming interruption, he felt something in himself akin to a gesture. Daily, he tried to identify whatever it was he half-proposed to do. It was like stepping forward – that was the closest he could come. He had made plans, constructed tactics, to stop the harm he was doing. He'd thought about giving up drink.

Perhaps there were ways of enlisting her help, or offering some sort of hint. He suspected that she had her own plans. Nothing was predictable except her manner of devising silences while his apologies were absorbed.

When he emerged, she was sitting on the wall, chin on knees, her arms crossed on her bare shinbones. The video in his head clicked and the tape started to roll. She lay under the man, her knees sharply angled and clasped in either hand to keep them hoisted. His mouth covered hers and their cheeks grew hollow. Then her hands dropped to his arse and pressed; he raised his torso to help with the angle. Her mouth opened in the two or three seconds that brought her to the edge, until she shouted into his face, wide-eyed with pleasure. The man slowed his stroke, letting the sensation spread and settle. He dropped his head and browsed on her breast, kissing the nipple cleanly. After a time, he gazed at her steadfastly until she looked directly up at him. They both smiled. He began to work into her again. She gave a small croak of approval and folded her legs on his back. It was all logged: the interior, the time of year, the name. He didn't even try to guess what these involuntary agonies were costing him. On each occasion he felt as if he were biting pieces out of his own face.

She watched him step out of the umbra of the doorway into the light and walk over counting his change with an expression of gloomy aggression. It made her smile. She cared for him enough to want to make him happy, but he seemed to lack the talent for that. It required too simple a vocabulary. Sometimes, particularly when she had wilfully hurt him, she had to consciously remind herself of her feelings: like counting blessings. Loving him was an outmoded thing, contradictory and oddly virtuous; it was a sort of patriotism.

2

You could tell from the photographs they took just how hot it was: a piercing white statue of the saint on its plinth near the harbour wall; the stone shone; she knelt to set it against a back-drop of noonday sky while he wound down the car windows.

A mile or so from Marsalforn he saw the Christ atop a scrub-cluttered hill. He judged it to be at least fifty feet tall. The arms were outstretched in blessing or supplication. She pulled over and he got out with the camera, standing on the bonnet to line up the shot. She wagged the front of her blouse to make a draught and watched his knees flexing.

'It'll be a dot.'

'Will it?' He bent and peered at her through the windscreen, seeking more advice.

'From this distance. Just a smudge.'

'I suppose so.' He tried a few more angles, but didn't press the shutter-release.

Much later, after their lunch and the wine they had agreed, that morning, to forego, he came to on the rock they'd scouted for – secluded so that she could take off her bikini-top – and said: 'I could have climbed up to it and taken a picture.'

'Why didn't you?' Her breasts and the strap lines were salmon-pink, the rest a deep brown. She trailed her hand across her belly where the perspiration itched, then eased the crotch of her briefs with a fore-finger. 'I'd have driven on and found a table.'

'Well, it would have been a bit of a walk.'

'Don't be wet.'

'I didn't think of it,' he said.

She sat up to get the bottle of sun-cream and shaded her eyes. 'You've burned.' She had been using his shirt and shorts as a pillow. Now she tossed them over, looking concerned. 'You'd better cover up.'

His skin crawled as he put the clothes on and shuffled into the triangle of shade near her head. She held out the bottle. 'Do my back while you're there.' To make it easy, she sat up and turned away, dangling her legs over the water. A windsurfer rounded the outcrop of rock and when he saw them, manoeuvred to a halt, stepping round the *planche* to change direction. Holding his balance, the man looked at her, lowering his sail a little to lose the wind, then beyond her for a moment to where he crouched applying the cream. The board drifted in until it was no more than twenty feet away; the man's eyes were fixed on her; his feet trod the *planche* to keep it stable. She held her hair up while he smoothed cream across her shoulders until it clarified, then patted her to let her know it was done. Swinging her legs round, she knelt to rearrange her towel and finally subsided, sighing, her shining back presented to the sun.

'Another fifteen minutes – okay?'

'Yes, fine.' He rummaged in their tote-bag for a book. When he looked up, marking his place with a finger, the windsurfer was headed away, raising a wake as he took the breeze further out.

Going back, she slowed the car, but didn't stop, when they reached the stretch of road that gave the best view of the hill. 'Too late now.'

'Yes.' The wind was cool. He shivered as he leaned out of the window for a clear look. The outlines were odd. The robe was a solid T; the long oval above it, he read as a fall of hair; but then it seemed rods protruded from the full sleeves: thin and rigid and without hands. It might have been modern, or vandalized, or crudely done.

'It's extraordinary.' As if in response, she brought the car to a near-halt. He wondered if he might be making too much of the thing: might seem precious. He said: 'It is curious, isn't it?'

She nodded. 'They're a very seriously religious people I gather.'

He felt chilled, his skin burning and prickling, so he wound the window up. 'Southern Catholicism,' he said. 'Irresistible.'

'Oh?' She speeded up. 'I thought you inclined to the hard men of the north. Lindisfarne, hair-shirts, winnowings to the bone – all that.'

'Yes. There's something about the southern version. It's indulgent, corrupt. I don't know . . . it attracts me when I see it.'

'Or childish.'

'Oh, yes; that too. In theory, I find it contemptible.' He was thinking of the blaze of neon haloes they'd seen in Venice; the charred remains of a martyr beneath an altar looking like ossified roots, and a foot in its glass box. Relics, all over the city, packaged like putrefying orchids. 'How far, would you say, does superstition stand from faith?'

She glanced sideways, noticing the lack of draught from his window, then back at the road as she fumbled for the sidelights. 'Oh dear,' she said, 'I'm afraid you're going to suffer.'

3

When he took his clothes off, she hissed through her teeth and laughed sympathetically. 'Oh dear.' Apart from the shallow vee that had been protected by his trunks, he was uniformly scarlet.

'Shit,' he said softly. In the mirror, dimly lit, he was almost luminous. His skin twitched. There were strong, intermittent pains and it burned; he felt as if he were standing too close to an immense electric fire. His teeth chattered.

He lay for half an hour in a brimming bath of cold water while she stayed on her bed, reading. To break her silence, he called out for a brandy. 'Do you think you should?' she asked, pouring it into a tooth-glass.

'It's that or sex. Or both.' He climbed out of the bath and took the glass. 'Any distraction . . .'

She handed him a towel. 'How about dinner? Any good?' She had changed into black silk trousers and a white shirt that showed off her tan. They dined at the fish place, their favourite, under vines and lapped by bougainvillea and he shook so that his knees kept rapping the underside of the table. Then they drove back to the hotel and she took him to the bar for his eighth or ninth brandy. A formica-topped circle had been laid down for dancing. They sat at the bar and watched the same three couples quickstep to everything the band played then – at his insistence – went out and bopped to a ragged rendition of *Don't It Make My Brown Eyes Blue?* He was feverish and had to bite his lower lip to keep his mouth still.

In the room, he took another from the mini-bar, then undressed in a rush, yelling. She looked at him, standing at the foot of her bed, arms held away from his sides, his cock up and ticking with pressure. 'You're mad,' she said, lying back and parting her legs, using a finger to make herself ready. He bent over so that she could wet him, briefly, then covered her. She jacked her thighs away from his burning flanks. He moved slowly, allowing her nothing. She looked up at him, interestedly. When he started to come, she asked, 'Doesn't it hurt?', intrigued, as if she were watching someone being tattooed. He slumped, without resting on her. Her heels slid down the counterpane. He thought that the only way he would get through it would be by talking all night, sitting out on the balcony, maybe, drinking water, registering the moment-by-moment relief as his skin cooled towards morning, waiting for the sky to dim and lose its darkness, then grow increasingly pale until it gained the tinge of a lighter blue and the sun lit what it could touch from the horizon, but her eyes had already begun to flutter and the tiny wheeze beneath each indrawn breath lengthened as her limbs relaxed.

Michael Hofmann

Six Poems

MICHAEL HOFMANN was born in 1957 in Freiburg, West Germany, and now lives in London. *Nights in the Iron Hotel*, his first book of poems, was published in 1983 by Faber & Faber. The following poems are new and hitherto unpublished.

Day of Reckoning

When we drove across America, going West,
I tanned through the sandwich glass windscreen.
Though I was eight, and my legs weren't yet long
in their long pants, I could still sit in front –

your co-driver who couldn't spell you . . .
My jagged elbow stuck out of the right-hand window,
I kept a tough diary, owned a blunt knife,
and my mother sat in the back with the girls.

I can't remember if we talked or if, even then,
you played the radio, but when I got tired
I huddled in my legroom in the Chevy *Belair*,
and watched the coloured stars under the dashboard . . .

I learned fractions from you in a single day,
multiplying and dividing. In Kingston, Ontario,
I had a cruel haircut. For you, it was a dry time –
in two years one short play about bankruptcy:

Let Them Down, Gently. There followed the great crash

Bavarian Afternoon

'Deutschland ist Hamlet'
Ferdinand von Freiligrath, 1844

I

Spiked *Pickelhaube* of the church, onion-dome
of the brewery – the beer and tits of Bavaria,

bulging the Iron Curtain like Polonius ...
his expensive foible for curiosity and security.

Computer-controlled and holding hands, jets scream past
every hour on the hour, like Old Faithful gushing.

II

Square houses, triangle roofs, round arches
of supermarkets – the architecture is pure geometry.

Lace curtains in the windows are a film of illusion,
a crocheted haze affording a diaphanous privacy.

Tropical plants breed ozone for sitting-rooms;
waving fronds camouflage the tanks of these resentful fish ...

III

Punctually, it starts raining in the picturesque street.
Its pastels darken, the pavement thirsts for dust.

The owner of a jeans-shop stands in his doorway.
His legs stay dry, but his paunch gets wet.

The German idyll walks past: Hansel and Gretel –
bedraggled parricides, bleached angels in denim and khaki.

A Walk in the Dark   (for R.S.W.)

My middle-aged clothes will outlast the irony
with which I wear them ... To be equable and pacific
at twenty-six, and borrow my father's tranquillised smile!
I have to imagine the incredulity I owe myself ...

After nightfall, I go on a constitutional in the park.
There is a group of Italians on the plank bridge,
someone says something, I see a hand grasp
at a silent breast, and start pushing it around.

The wind foams through the tree-tops, and blows away
the brewery smell of roasting grain, hops and malt –
the highest natural specifications! A flurry of rain.
The path is a crisp shale, like ground-up shells,

nowhere near the sea ... A modern orphanage
has crucifixes and the institution's pumpkin curtains
in its windows. The *Biedermeier* architecture
is helmeted, bulbous, encrusted – suburban homes

for oysters, crabs and hermits, home for Thomas Mann ...
Though now, speech therapists, dentists and tax inspectors
have driven him out, the obdurate owner of villas,
old ephebophile and paterfamilias, master of disguise!

Three boys on mopeds nip past in a storm of dust and exhaust –
the aromatic distillation of ice-cream vans and summer.
In their headlights, I am seventeen, sleeping rough,
near Perpignan ... The last frontier! We walked out of town

with our rucksacks and stopped by the cloacal river.
All night, we were terrorised by revving motor-bikes,
their snuffling lights tracking us down as we lay
stretched between pines on the bald, needled earth.

(Munich)

Snowdrops

The days are so dark they hardly count –
but they must have some marginal warmth after all,
for the drizzle of my night-breath turns to fog.

The window is opaque, a white mirror affirming
life goes on inside this damp lung of a room . . .
I have no perspective on the dotty winter clouds,

the pubic scrub of this street I am growing to hate,
with its false burglar alarms and sleeping policemen.
My exhalations blot out the familiar view.

I can tell without looking when your car draws up,
I know its tune as it reaches the end of its tether
and stops under the lamp-post, melodramatic and old-red,

the unwilling gift of your sainted grandmother
who disliked you and died suddenly on Friday.
'*Grand-merde*' you called her when you left sometimes

to go with her to visit your uncle in hospital,
lying there with irreversible brain damage
almost as long as I've lived here, after

falling downstairs drunk. You chat to him,
and imagine or fail to imagine that he responds
when you play him the recording of his greatest moment

when the horse he trained won the Derby.
I stay here and listen to sport on the radio,
a way of processing time to trial and outcome.

Someone brought me some cigarettes from America
called *Home Run*, and they frighten me half to death
in their innocuous vernal packaging, green and yellow.

Birds of Passage

'The slash of rain. Outside the window, blackbirds
shoot around like dark clouds in the sycamore.
It is meat and drink to them. Between its leaves,
the sky is silver paper, the end of their world . . .

I stare away. I don't want to watch the circus
of my husband's homecoming, a bankrupt show
of defensiveness, guilt and irritability . . .
Two routes in his head, two itineraries, two women.'

The Lower Depths

Des Esseintes himself would have admired
her fastidiousness – anorexia, years in hospital –
as he gloated over his own peptone enemas . . .
Her horror is a purely physical matter.
If she had her way, it would all cease.

Like sticks of furniture swathed in sheets,
her limbs ghost about the place, longing for peace,
disuse. She walks fast to lose weight –
a blue streak, hoping for invisibility
behind '60's dyed hair and false eyelashes.

In a gesture of self-betrayal, she goes shopping:
powdered milk, Gitanes, cans of cat-food
to placate Sappho, her black panther of a cat . . .
A Japanese lodger lived there for a while.
In his country, there are many centenarians –

rice, raw fish, and the subjugation of women
combine to promote longevity in the male.
A dietary expert, he drank as much beer
in an evening as a special *kobe* beef cow.
He never cleaned the bath, and left rich stains

in the lavatory bowl, like a dirty protest . . .
She has a boyfriend of sorts, weird, well-spoken,
Jesus-bearded. His childhood squints from one eye.
Something out of Dostoevsky, he wears only
navy blue – the colour of religious aspirants.

An anonymous depressive, he talks her into knots.
. . . Often, he isn't allowed in to see her.
Then his notes bristle on the doormat like fakirs,
her name on them in big block capitals,
widely spaced on the paranoid envelope . . .

Desmond Hogan

Alan's Novel

DESMOND HOGAN is thirty-two. He was born in County Galway and lives in London. His second novel, *The Leaves on Grey*, is available in paperback with Picador, as are his two collections of stories, *The Diamonds at the Bottom of the Sea* (for which he won the 1980 John Llewellyn Rhys Memorial Prize) and *Children of Lir*, in a one-volume edition called *Stories*. His latest novel, *A Curious Street*, from which this extract is taken, will be published by Hamish Hamilton.

Author's Note

'Alan's Novel' is the summary of a novel I always thought I'd write myself, but as I began writing, it became that of a character in a different novel, Alan Mulvanney's novel. Alan was a school teacher in Athlone who, in my novel *A Curious Street*, dies by his own hand in September 1977. From his childhood he was obsessed with Irish history and this novel represented his attempt to be creative with Irish history. But on finishing it in the early 1940s, he did a strange thing. He locked it in a drawer. But he told the story to the mother of Jeremy Hitchens, who narrates *A Curious Street*, and she, living later in Leeds and married to an Englishman, passed it on to her son as she would have passed on any Irish folk story. In *A Curious Street* Alan's novel and other ikons gather to cause an obsession, as involved as Alan's, in the narrator. This extract is one of the first fragments in *A Curious Street*. Jeremy Hitchens goes back to a dark night in the autumn of 1943 when a young man told his mother the story of 'A Cavalier Against Time', a manuscript in a nearby drawer, as if letting her in on a salacious secret. What follows is the narrator's attempted illumination of that tale.

*L*orcan O'Mahony was born in Pludd Street near Shoemaker's Tower in Galway city 10 December 1619. His father fittingly was a shoemaker and his mother of Catholic, Gaelic origin. Right from the beginning he had a streak of dark hair on his head which distinguished him.

When he was very small his mother would place him on a stool, she herself standing upright, bun intact, her figure draped in a penitential gown, and tell him tales of Ireland's past, of Gerald Fitzgerald, cripple on horseback, hewn down in Munster, his ghost still flying, eyeless sockets gleaming, his lands confiscated from his posterity, the osprey leaping, pheasant flitting lands of Munster dredged and drained by English newcomers, laburnum instead of the wild hawthorn, and the poet Edmund Spenser, 'that bandy legged dwarf' Lorcan's mother called him, admiring his Goddess Moon in Kilcolman. Everywhere the English were moving in and the Irish being ousted. The bulk of the stories Lorcan's mother told were about the vigil of Ireland, that lady in green with diamonds sewn onto the edges of her dress, for foreign aid. In 1579 James Fitzmaurice landed in Kerry with arms from the pope, wandering about Kerry, proclaiming his descent from Thomas à Becket and waving a banner which showed Christ crowned with thorns and dripping blood, until he was murdered by a Burke. In 1580 Italians and Portuguese ensconced themselves at Dún an Óir before being hacked like seals by English generals. The Spanish Armada approached in 1588 and Lorcan's mother delighted in describing how some of its survivors were beheaded on Saint Augustine's Hill in Galway, their bodies wrapped in linen at night by the people of Galway. One young man escaped the massacre, was sheltered by a local family but his memories proved too much for him and one day, gibbering and mad, in a black cloak, he walked into the hills to be devoured by O'Flahertys or wild boars. The Spanish made a final unsuccessful bid on Ireland in 1601 and after that the last great earls of Ulster, O'Neill and O'Donnell, left, their red and watery eyes witnessing a vision of Christ over Croagh Patrick as they passed that mountain in an untrustworthy vessel; their boat chased by the English outside Galway; their bodies lying now in the Franciscan Convent of San Pietro in Montorio, Rome; their sculpted hands in repose under Raphael's *Transfiguration*; the soul of Ireland dead among the burnished golds of Renaissance Italy.

The effects of this death were felt in Galway as Lorcan was growing up. Once known as the 'Thebes of the Western World' now its population looked wistfully to an ocean which no longer readily brought wine and silk from Spain, ivory from Africa, spices from India. Merchants went by holding their flagging bellies. A Catholic town, it had been the first to prostrate itself at the feet of Protestantism. The people of Galway had allowed the lord deputy to tie his horses in Saint Nicholas's Church in 1534. The Gaelic chieftains had kissed the ring of Elizabeth on a gold cushion here. Its hinterland always having been denied, now that hinterland moved closer, men in wolf-skins, women lean like starving calves rubbing shoulders with the city. In 1596 O'Donnell had surrounded the town but was driven off by a mad nun who had threatened to curse him with syphilis. Now the terms of siege had changed. Although a Catholic queen reigned, nuns hurried like dormice at dawn and priests celebrated Mass among rocks where seals were slaughtered at Michaelmas. Religion was the bartering table, and the traditional but waning wealth of Galway the prize. A woman played a strange tune on a flageolet in Blake's Lane and dust settled on the black cloak of a blind woman.

To escape this unease Lorcan would run through the streets of Galway in early morning, nearly stumbling once or twice into an Italian merchant who prodded along with a diamond-topped stick, by-passing the Cataracts where men fished with spears, fleeting along a beach where donkeys carried cargoes of seaweed, confronting the ocean where he expected a Spanish vessel to rise, sails ethereal like fairy goblets, though all that usually emerged above the horizon were cloud formations like Ferdia, like Oisín.

When he was nine his mother brought him to a place of pilgrimage in the north, clinging to him on a mule's back; Gaelic tribes crossing their path with lean, shaggy cattle; charred spots on the hills where corn was burned to separate the wheat from the chaff; women on stools plucking the wool from sheep's backs. They crossed in a currach to an island where they crawled on bare knees over stones; rising at dawn, penance done, to dance to bagpipe music. What Lorcan would remember about this place however was a gate to Hell closed down by decree of a pope because the visions of those who entered were so tormenting: devils warming their naked backsides over quivering fires, bishops with faces half of toadstools and croziers of fungus-eaten trees, remorseless personal memories.

His mother and father were swept away in a plague the following year and Lorcan was adopted by an aunt who'd turned Protestant to marry an English merchant, one of the class who'd come to take over the apple-blossom-crowded, brook-gurgling monasteries of Ireland. This lady did not look unlike Ireland herself, jewels sewn onto the edges of her red dress, raven hair in a bun, an eloquent distance between her pale breasts. She and her husband lived in a Dutch red brick house with dormer windows near Athenry but because of the many sieges they moved into the house in Pludd Street, re-tiling the floor.

Lorcan was taught Euclid by a Protestant minister in black, standing upright in a small room, hands behind his back. More often than not he managed to escape, chasing butterflies down Martin's Mill Lane, overhearing the voice of a teacher in the Gaelic school of Alexander Lynch. 'In the year 30 after Christ some fifteen of his followers landed in West Connaught with five geese, two chickens, a pig. They set about building a house near a stream between two hills and preaching his word.' Young men lay on rushes on the floor. A solitary light came through a lattice window.

In 1634 Wentworth, the lord deputy, rode into Galway on a mule, grinning like an Italian puppet. Already there were rumours. He sat in the castle of the Earl of Clanricarde in Portumna, feet on the oak table. He was after land for the king. He had three Galway lawyers look into the king's title in Galway and when they found against the king he had them thrown into jail; one of them perished, and the other two on their release assigned one third of the lands of Galway to the king. A dead whale lay on a beach and Lorcan's aunt died.

She died screaming. Keening women waited, their turnip faces grinning, a proselyte about to go down to Hell. White horses with black plumes on their heads cantered at her funeral and ran away with the coffin. Lightning stood in the air, a tableau, and the sea raged against an English garrison.

A young man journeyed up to Dublin in the 1630s, haunted by the antiquated voice of a teacher in the Gaelic school of Alexander Lynch and by the red scarf of one of the new English preachers; the teacher describing early Christians bringing fragments of Christ's cross to

Connemara and the preacher's hands raised to the paltry Atlantic sun, his black figure trembling in one of Galway's squares as his sermon boasted of a new age based on love and brotherhood and the sun.

A student in black, Lorcan sat in a room in Trinity College with a hawk. It was not uncommon to see soldiers chase Carmelite priests caught saying Mass through the streets or to hear Protestant bishops in Christ Church rail against the Catholic population: 'Happy shall he be who taketh and dasheth thy children against the storm', to see men urinating in the corners, clerics getting drunk in the cellars below, while by Saint Patrick's Cathedral the gentlefolk of Dublin tripped over pigs' guts from the nearby tanneries to hear more sober sermons. Wherever he went, through the streets filled with gooseberries in early summer, with Malahide oysters in winter, in the taverns overrun with actors from the New Theatre in Werburgh Street and whores, Lorcan could still hear them, two voices, a direction. A fat, drunken chancellor was driven in a carriage from County Cork to Trinity and Lorcan took off for Italy, a typical student of the time. A student from Oxford insulted him on the Ponte Vecchio for being Irish. He was assailed by fumes of portraits of young men fumigated to rid them of typhoid. Jesuits, seeking to convert him, chased him amid the storm of gold of the Vatican Square, cloaks raised above their heads. But he couldn't stop remembering and, on the force of an intuition, he returned to Galway, swept on a white horse into the Connemara countryside, past eddying tides of red deer, until he came to the castle of Eleanor O'Keefe near Renvyle.

Her people had left Kerry in the previous century, driven out by the English, departing from the hills rustling with red dresses and resounding with the 'Te Deum', crossing the Shannon in currachs made of cows' hides, birds of winter and snow dangling, arriving here, a rainbow. Swans hovered in the bay behind and little boats took off from a gully to larger boats, which hurried to Europe. Eleanor, a red-headed girl with eyes that gleamed the secretive green of dark bottles in Galway wineshops, stood at the door as though she'd been expecting him for a long time.

Apart from Eleanor, only her brother lived here with his Welsh foster-brother, both albinos, the two of them sleeping together on a mat of rushes. Their faces, eyes, piece upon frail piece, looked to the sea, querulously. Priests came from and went to Europe, little, bald, agitated men ruminating over words left by an early Christian sect who had frequented this area. 'If you give birth to what is within you, you will be saved. If you do not give birth to what is within you,

you will perish.' Eleanor refilled their glasses with red wine. The two boys stared at cards which showed witches and minstrels, and the priests hurried off to Europe, their findings under their arms, fearful lest their investigations were not completed before an oncoming calamity.

Lorcan went back and forth, becoming Eleanor's lover, the two of them sleeping together on the kitchen floor, a brook running through, a Brigid's cross over the door, rushes in the eaves, their love-making fragmentary, the feathers, wings, lineaments of swans.

Early in 1641 there was a deluge of rats in Ireland. Later in the year a manifestation of caterpillars in Moycullen, a sure sign. In October the Catholics of Ulster rose – rumours of babies roasting on spits – the people of Galway declared for the king but later, the governor away, seized the garrison. They surrendered at the entreaties of the Earl of Clanricarde. The English, however, were not satisfied with a simple submission and came in seventeen ships, burning the bones of the dead at Saint Dominic's Monastery, murdering lone boatmen. The people of Galway rose again, seizing the garrison again, ordering two cannons from France, sending delegates to the new Catholic parliament in Kilkenny.

In 1643 the churches were reopened, a giant cross erected on Great Middle Street for the Corpus Christi procession – priests in red and white treading on roses of Sharon, singing the 'Te Deum' in unison – a huge, unwieldy alligator.

That was the point at which Lorcan, Eleanor, the two boys left the castle in Connemara, veering north, collecting a Protestant bishop in Mayo, encircling the north coast, all the time preaching a gospel based on the pacifism of early Christians in Connemara and the teachings of the new English preachers as compounded for Lorcan, by candlelight in a Dublin inn, by a young English actor from the New Theatre in Werburgh Street, who spoke of the dispossessed of England stirring among the fens, the forests, reclaiming the earth. Wherever they went they heard stories of atrocities in the recent rebellion – naked men, women and children pushed into icy waters, pregnant women tied to chairs as dartboards, pious women buried alive in potato fields. They passed a spot where a young man had waited helplessly in the previous century as his family were slaughtered on a nearby island, swans standing in the air, a forewarning graffiti. They rested near a castle where a Protestant bishop had been buried by the O'Neills and, so loved by them, lamented with kettle drums and bagpipes though they had caused his death by imprisoning him for a winter in a castle with cannon ball holes in the walls. They warmed themselves over vagrants' fires – Lorcan's face lucid with flame – listening to stories of the old days, hot wine with ginger, nutmeg and burnt sugar. The two boys held hands, drinking water out of stone goblets. The Protestant bishop murmured in his sleep. Eleanor slept on Lorcan's shoulder as he sat awake. They were welcomed by a gentle family, marching up an avenue of cypress trees, the fires squashed out, the stones cold, the lady of the house wandering about in a lace nightdress, reciting her childhood prayers. A wandering lute player entertained them with 'Lady Hunsun, Her Galliard', and they moved on towards Dublin on roads naked men, women and children had converged upon in the recent rebellion.

They spent the winter in Dublin when the Liffey broke its banks, playing perilous games of chess in an inn near Oxmanton, heading south again come spring, passing English soldiers warming themselves with ikons of mother and child thrown into fires, overhearing Irish soldiers with knife-edge eyes move among the trees, encountering a landscape smouldering with war and crawling with lost women and children.

Near Castlecomer they had the most terrible sight of all. Under a pigmy tree an old woman ate a baby as though it was chicken bones.

They preached on, young man and woman on the same white horse, two boys in love, an unwieldy Protestant bishop, a strange circus which prevailed against a landscape of famine and war, drawing an audience of women holding children, of men with mouths blackened from eating nettles, disappearing again, leaving their audience more confused than before on the outskirts of some village.

They were left alone until they came to North Cork and there the two boys, lagging behind, were murdered, their bodies found hugging one another, sheep's bodies tarnished in blood, and later the Protestant bishop was killed in an ambush. Lorcan and Eleanor, surveying him, a disarray of vestments, knew they'd be blamed but they rode on. By now they were legendary, young man and woman on the same white horse preaching peace, a spectral pair. People waited on the outskirts of villages for them. But their audience betrayed them by dying. They wandered for days and weeks through black bog and forest, past clumps of red berries, climbing hills slit by lake and pool, challenging cloud, affronted by raucous jackdaws, swathed in soft rain. They found no one and eventually preached to one another. Eleanor lying on Lorcan's shoulder was hit by a solitary flake of snow on a mountaintop one day and they fled to her castle in Connemara which was already pillaged by war.

There they survived on periwinkles picked from the shore and swans killed by a musket Lorcan had purchased from a gibbering beggar. Swans fell from the air, white corpses. They approached tentatively. A primeval Irish curse settles on those who eat swan's meat but they feasted on the delicious fragments, roasting them on spits. Eleanor smiled as Lorcan handed her morsels, her red hair flaming against the fading Atlantic sun. Come twilight they told stories to one another over the fire, Lorcan retelling the tales of Homer and Virgil, Eleanor filling in the gaps of history, describing how King John when he came to Ireland met Ruanus who had lived since the time of the Flood and how Solinus, the Roman historian, had thought the Irish Sea to be navigable for only a few weeks in summertime. At night they slept close, reverberations of wine from the cellar below, the sea pounding in, sounds of war coming closer. In the morning they'd rise, kill more swans, devouring them. They spent a winter here and a spring. A Spanish wreck magically washed up, and whales went south. Eleanor walked the shore as though she'd had a surfeit of wine. Eventually they tired of their diet and took refuge in Galway. That winter it was hit by a plague and they followed the townsfolk into the hills where they waited until Our Lady's Day when the plague lifted and the people returned like dreamers to a town where grass grew on the doorsteps.

Events in Ireland were furious and hard to follow. One day Butler rode into Kilkenny, accepted as leader by the Catholic Confederates, the deeds of his ancestors proclaimed on the walls. The next day the spit-fire Rinuccini swept in, incarcerating those who had supported Butler, declaring himself leader in an upsurge of red robes. Munster was being devastated and Connaught laid waste, right up to the point it was waste anyway. Then Cromwell came.

Lorcan and Eleanor, living in the house in Pludd Street, Lorcan's uncle dead, heard the stories with trepidation. Drogheda was ransacked, gentlewomen hacked as they proffered their jewels on their knees, pregnant women with swords through their wombs, hands clasping mother-of-pearl rosaries in the mud, men, women and children perishing in Saint Peter's Church, the flame of gunpowder merging with the scarlet of a cavalier's cloak and the rage of blood on the Boyne.

In Wexford monks rose from the massacre into the sky, resting on clouds, their hands piously joined in prayer. In Cloughoughter the Catholic general Eóghen Ruadh O'Neill died on the ground, first revealing the Dominican garb under his military uniform. In Clonmacnoise Catholic bishops cried out against Cromwell at a synod among the ruins. But the Cromwellians forged on. Limerick was besieged, men hanged at its gate. Then Galway surrounded.

Lorcan stood over Eleanor as she sat, like any lord with his lady in a portrait of the time, except that their clothes were peeling and their skin festering.

Priests raised the host among congregations of rats and a whole convent of nuns took to witchcraft in desperation.

Lorcan and Eleanor knew they had to get out before it was too late. Ladies swept in and out of inns, their noses in the air, consumptive children holding their trains, the ladies oblivious to the stench of corpses because of the position of their noses and the profusion of perfumes which surrounded them. A Quaker lady was murdered by O'Flaherty youths as she knelt at prayer on a prie-dieu, her head used as a football. A ship bearing corn nearly broke through the blockade but was offset. Some men seeking cattle outside the city gates were murdered. Then the siege broke. The Parliamentarians marched in, Palm Sunday 1652.

Eleanor managed to escape dressed as a soldier, marching out with other soldiers, wolfhounds alongside them, kettle drums beating, a solitary bagpiper lamenting them into exile as a ship waited. Lorcan slipped out the opposite direction in a priest's garb, encountering the native Irish as they flooded west before Cromwell's men, witnessing their weddings and their wakes, among stones, among brooks, an absolute defiance to fate. He was captured as a priest, imprisoned in white in Inishbofin while awaiting transportation to the West Indies, again escaped, this time in a currach with a bishop who'd held an ikon of mother and child from Saint Nicholas's Church in Galway under the clay of his cabin. Starting off from a nearby island, step by step, Lorcan got as far as Scotland, crossing Scotland, reaching Europe. There he began his search for Eleanor. They'd made a pact. She wore his onyx ring. They'd married under a white hawthorn tree beside black bog water in the presence of the two boys and the Protestant bishop.

In Paris, Irish noblemen walked by with holes in their hose and Butler, the flaxen haired, was rumoured to live on a pistole a week. Crowds surged angrily around the coach of a sparrow-like cardinal and Lorcan moved on to Brussels. There Irish noble-ladies were ensconced in the Convent of the Feuillantines. He headed east. In the Palatine May Day was still celebrated, flowers about cows' udders, fires in the hills. The further east he went the more demented puppets on village greens became. All the time a picture formed, that of a portrait of a young man holding a medallion remembered from Italy. In Poland, clouds of war raging, he turned back. Back in Paris Irish noblemen had become drunker and more slovenly, one of them insulting Lorcan from a sidewalk. An Irish noble family, fallen on good times, invited him to their home, feeding him and clothing him. The young girl of the house, albino herself, played the harpsichord, singing 'Thugamar Féin an Samradh Linn' – 'We bring the Summer with Us' – and the lady of the house mourned the old days though no one knew what or where the old days were any more. Lorcan stood over the harpsichord, glass of red wine in his hand in a familiar gesture, and at the end of the evening a dwarfed servant handed him an address. In Antwerp he found Eleanor, bedecked in jewellery, married to a merchant, not wanting to see him.

He thrust south, all the time thinking of the stories they had told one another around Ireland to send one another to sleep, of young Irish soldiers all around Europe telling the same stories over camp-fires to keep one another awake for the next battle, of swans falling from the air, a vanquished heritage.

One day he mounted a hill, saw the sea and heard a flamenco song, the voice of the flamenco merging with the lamentation of women in Galway and the music of a curlew as a young man and woman on horseback, two boys, a Protestant bishop passed a lake in Ireland. Lorcan O'Mahony had found a home.

He married a Moroccan girl, started a timber business in Sevilla, lived until the Bourbons came to power. An old man, nearly blind, he'd sit in a garden among the orange trees and the purple Judas trees listening to his grandchildren play, his eyes still aflame, the blue of the sea around Saint Macdara's Island on a fine summer's morning. Irish priests would come tripping from the Royal College of the Noble Irish in Salamanca with the latest ill-tidings from Ireland; Aughrim, the coming of the magpies from Wales, the penal laws, the accession of the bonhav-faced queen. But all the time his mind would not be on war and devastation but on a young man and woman on a white horse preaching peace and how the years had plucked out their idealism and mutilated their love like a portrait of a young man with the eyes torn out.

James Lasdun

Six Poems

JAMES LASDUN was born in London in 1958. His stories and poems have appeared in various publications including *Firebird I, Twofold* and the *Literary Review*. He received an Eric Gregory Award for his poetry in 1982.

Vindice at the Oyster Bar

Here they come, the silver-haired boys,
Minds glandular, tuned to the brine of sex,
Bullion at flinty wrists, carbuncled fingers,
Silk scarves afloat on scalloped necks –

You foolish girls, so willingly deceived,
What do you seek, to what ghost of bliss
Glimpsed beyond silver do you cling? Rose flesh
Turning to carrion for the next jackal's kiss . . .

A parable: watch light blade down through blinds
To tongue bright morning's tocsin from a jar
And coax a glass-hard tulip's metal scarlet,
The belling petals' aztec star –

One day you touch the flower, and each petal
Drops from the stem unblemished, hard, with all
Its moon-curve, pristine glaze immaculate,
You almost hear them clatter as they fall –

That is the unimpeachable life;
To quit before the years' contusions bloom,
Unheralded, each second like the spider's
Perilous march across a crowded room;

Then watch those crayfish in the bubbling tank,
Curled peach-fire torsos peppered like your wrist,
Splayed samurai tails, the stripped-flex feelers
Beckoning what the body must resist;

More intimacy than nature will allow –
Look at them grope, and probe, and interlace
Through drifts of snapped antennae, severed limbs,
Love fused to violence in the one embrace;

I see your backs thrash, limbs flail, as theirs do
When the bare-armed scullion wrenches one pair
Out from that slow, obscene, dissolution,
Into the quick, asphyxiating air ...

Above Laggan

Low sun, low mist, long shadows probe the water,
Wild cotton flares in the contracting dusk,
The harebells flex to voltage in the stalk
And wheatgerm stiffens in its husk –
Down on the fallow field the rabbits scatter,
Maddened by the shadow of a hawk.

Whoever looks desires that proximate death;
To flare like matchlight, stiffen, flex or run,
Somehow to evade the supernumerary,
To have one's shadow lengthened by the sun
And hold, elect, one's tenantry of earth
Whereof all things are but a colonie –

You could lie here imagining chance might fall
From nowhere, like a hawk, or that the wind,
To whose calligraphy the hill-grass yields,
Might write as vividly across the mind,
Leaving indelible the kestrel's call,
Cloud-shadow spreading stains across the fields.

Picture of a Girl

I lie on the dirty white candlewick
You so disliked, thinking of you at your best;
Among animals mostly – Absalom
Whose high, unearthly screech you mimicked once
So fluently, he swooped from his chimney perch
To strut before us on the rain-fresh lawn,
Rustling green plumage as if a mate
Had bloomed there like the cepes and chanterelles . . .
And then the cats; Babette, whose dynasty
Had frayed the Morris hangings into shreds –
I remember you struggling to hold all twelve
Still in your lap for a photograph;
That night you giggled quietly in your sleep –
Lovely transparent dreamer, I could see
The singed-beige kittens tumbling there again . . .

Now I recede, the years are like rough stones
Glazed to a moonstone glimmer by the sea,
Fantastical – Absalom cries again,
I hear that garden crackling in the rain,
Pale dusty green mimosa's saffron burrs
Turning to paste as they brush our clothes,
Quicksilver raindrops on the soft peach furze –
We lived well, I remember starched linen,
Silver, the flayed blue hearts of hot-house figs,
My profligate goddess stooping where a marrow
Had burst with rain, and spilt its sequin seeds,
The clouds pitted like granite, but tissue-light,
Heaving their slow collisions in the skies,
And where the pond froze up one winter night
Big golden carp alive beneath the ice . . .

Crabs –

– whose flesh retracted from a violent shore
To lie beneath a carapace of bone,
Who lost the end of living in the means,
Each in its private military zone,

Paradigms of the exoskeletal
Whose armature and claws' serrated grip
Taught us technologies of the metal muscle,
Gave us machines to scavenge, crack or rip –

We netted crabs out from Menemsha Pond,
Risking our naked flesh against the bite
Of bladed oyster shells and hidden claws,
Crashing the gaudy creatures into light

Where, with their turquoise streaks and bevelled limbs
They seemed some dormant possibility
The mind had once considered as a shell
Against the issue of its own proclivity

To violence. They battled in the keep tank,
And later, when we pulled them out, we saw
They'd necklaced like a conjuror's magic hoops,
Leaving behind one frayed and severed claw –

We seek unlikeness as a close-hauled boat
That tempts the wind to spin it through its eye,
And if the wind should spin us as we seek,
What beasts will claim us as their ancestry?

But now we tame these ocean-graves, their flesh,
Twice dead, shall satisfy a gourmet's relish
For the nearly rank; tonight we'll eat them
Cased in the softer crusting of a quiche ...

On the Road to Chenonceaux

A grey Mercedes comes and vanishes,
Its hum declines along the empty road
Where melting pitch gleams through the surface dust,
Wind plays the light on rustling leaves – grey, green,
And a blue that isn't there, but seems to be.

Another azure flickers in the hedge,
Obscure behind a broidery of buds
And a scent that's lost as soon as it's discovered;
Elusive, but defined by its apparel,
Event that may have never taken place . . .

Beside the hedge, an unattended pile
Of watermelons catches and keeps the light
Among the deckled shadows of its orbs –
One is so huge, its rind has split apart
And through the gash pink darkens into scarlet

As if to show how sensuous is the core
Of all veiled things: look at the hedge again,
Find what eludes deficiency of sense,
Depict the known and not the imagined
Or the desired, and in a language of plain fact –

Radicle, plumule, and cotyledon
Cased in the integument of seed,
And the slow absorption of the mineral earth;
Carpel, stamen, petal, sepal and leaf,
Keys to unlock the doors of a given world . . .

Another car comes by and disappears,
Before it's gone, it shivers in the haze
Of heat that rises from the empty road;
The wind still plays the light from grey to green
Through a blue that isn't there, but seems to be.

Snake Burning

Indolent creature, do you not observe
How the air is clotting with locusts? Coil
Upon coil of you wreathes the dead acacia –
Such heavy lumber to shift, such toil
To unravel yourself, each loop and curve –

I know that tired complexity, I too
Would choose to think this heat the sun's alone –
Your tongue is mine, and we both taste burning
But lie as if our minds had turned to stone.
We could outsleep the limbs that cradle you.

Look now, the earth about you is alive:
Plum-sized shrews, the golden field mice
And spark-bright lizards scuttle past your jaws.
A hare stumbles against you, mazed butterflies
Gyrate. The air is humming like a hive,

Ground trembling beneath you, while overhead
In swift succession, deer and gazelle leap,
Trailing their shadows across your body –
Wisps of blue smoke arrive, and still you sleep;
What is it you and I cannot feel? Dread –

Until the fury is upon us: fire
Blazing in the grass, do you feel it now?
Pooled in your contortions, furnacing –
You flex and writhe, but you have become slow
And each nerve seems to sing like a plucked wire –

I watch you dying; are we so alike
Our deaths could be exchanged? I am entranced –
Your last prey – watching your glazed marquetry
Scorch, your body dance as it always danced,
Your diamond head thrown back as if to strike.

Bernard Mac Laverty

End of Season

The elder Miss Bradley left her briefcase against a bollard and walked to the end of the small pier. She stood listening to the sea coming in from below. White horses flecked the bay in the middle and the wind was strong enough to make her avert her face from its direction. She was convinced that the summer was over. A week back at school and already the first gale of winter. On this exposed coast autumn did not exist. With no trees apart from a few stunted thorns, how could it?

When it was not raining she liked to come here on her way home, particularly on windy days. It rinsed the experience of school from her. She did not stand long – a minute, perhaps two, her eyes closed facing into the wind until she began to be unsure of her balance. Then she would open them again to dispel the fear of toppling. The tail of her dress began to vibrate noisily. She turned on her heel and walked slowly to her briefcase, leaning back into the wind trying not to let its strength fluster her or make her movements awkward.

The briefcase was heavy with jotters and she wished she had brought the car. The school was only three quarters of a mile from the house but each day she debated whether or not she should walk the distance for the sake of her health. It would not do to have two invalids in the one house.

The family home was one of a terrace of cream-painted houses set back from the road behind long well-kept gardens. Some of the houses still had little gibbets overhanging the pavement with 'Bed & Breakfast' signs swinging in the wind. As she walked up the path she faintly heard her sister, Kathleen, laughing and thought it odd – a feeling which was increased when she opened the front door and smelt tobacco smoke. In the front room a man sat in her armchair beside the book-case, with his back to the light, talking.

'Ah Mary, there you are,' said her sister. The man stood up politely. 'You remember Mr Maguire?' She went along with Kathleen's prompt and smiled saying, 'Yes indeed,' and shook hands with him. In his other hand Mr Maguire held their old guest book. He sat down again and opened it so quickly that he must have had his finger in the place.

'I was just looking at when we were here last.' He passed the book to Mary. She found a Mr and Mrs Maguire whose stay was dated July 1958.

'We were on our honeymoon,' he said. 'We had only booked for one night but we stayed a week.' The man had a distinct Belfast accent.

'Mr Maguire thought we were still a guest-house,' said Kathleen.

'Oh no. We stopped that a long time ago.' Mary flicked to the last entry in the book. 'In 1971.' She set it on the sideboard and, rubbing her hands, moved close to the fire.

'It's like January,' she said. 'Is the kettle on?' Her sister asked Mr Maguire if he would have more tea.

'I wouldn't say no.' He handed over his empty cup and saucer and Kathleen rattled it on to the tray along with her own. She elbowed her way out the door to the kitchen leaving Mary and the stranger in silence.

'Are you looking for a place to stay?' Mary asked.

'Yes. I decided to treat myself to a holiday. It's years since I've gone anywhere.'

'Have you tried any of the other guest-houses?'

'No. This is where I wanted to come.'

'It was nice of you to remember us.'

'It's funny how well you remember good times, holidays,' he said. 'I'm sure you don't remember us. We would have been one couple in a crowded summer.'

'Yes, sometimes it's difficult. But I rarely forget a face. Names, yes.' Mary sat down on the hearth in a delicate side-saddle posture and shivered. From her low position she could see the man's polished shoes in the light that shone beneath the armchair. They were immaculate. Her mother had always told her that a man's footwear was the key to his character. 'Beware of someone with dirty shoes,' she had said. 'Even worse is the man who has polished his shoes but neglected to do his heels. But worst of all is the man with black polish stains on his socks. It's the ultimate sloth.' Mary looked up at him but his face was in shadow because his back was to the grey light from the window. He wore an open-necked shirt, a pair of trousers too light for his age and a blue sweater with a small emblem of a red jaguar on it. A casual kit – just the kind of thing wives buy for their husbands to take them away for a week's holiday.

'And Mrs Maguire?'

'My wife died last December.'

'Oh I'm sorry.'

'She had been ill for a long time. It was a merciful release.'

'Oh I am sorry,' she said. 'What brings you back to this part of the world?' He hesitated before answering.

'I wanted to see Spanish Point. Where the galleon went down. The *Girona*.'

'Yes, I walk out there frequently myself. There's nothing much. Rocks, sea.'

'I was at an exhibition in the museum of the stuff they brought up and I thought I'd just like to look at the place. Imagine it a bit.'

Kathleen's voice called loudly from the kitchen. Mary excused herself and went out.

'He wants to stay for a couple of nights,' whispered Kathleen. 'I told him I'd have to ask you. What do you think?'

'How do you feel about it? Can you cope?'

'Yes, I don't mind. The money would come in handy.' Mary was about to go back to the other room when her sister held her by the arm.

'But listen to this,' Kathleen laughed and wheezed. 'We had been talking about books. He tells me he reads a lot – as a matter of fact he's book mad – and when I came in with the tea I said, "Do you like Earl Grey?" and he says, "I don't know. What did he write?" Isn't that marvellous?' Mary smiled and nodded while Kathleen giggled uncontrollably. She said to herself, 'Stop it Kathleen,' and slapped the back of her wrist. She straightened her face and set out some more biscuits on a plate. Then she burst out laughing again.

'He kept talking about the eedgit, at one stage.'

'The what?'

'The book *The Eegit*. One of the big Russians. He meant *The Idiot*.'

'Oh,' said Mary.

'Really Kathleen, control yourself.' Again she straightened her face and picked up the tray. Mary opened the door for her.

'It'll be something for me to do,' Kathleen whispered over her shoulder as she led the way into the other room.

'That'll be fine Mr Maguire,' she said. 'If you'll give me a minute I'll fix up your room for you.' He edged forward in his seat and made a vague gesture as if to assist Ka̶t̶h̶l̶e̶e̶n̶ ̶w̶i̶t̶h̶ ̶t̶h̶e̶ tray.

'Thank you very much,' he said a̶s̶ ̶ . . . s̶i̶s̶t̶e̶r̶s̶.
'I'll try and cause . . .

on the tiled apron of the hearth to be near the fire. Mr Maguire sipped from his cup holding his saucer close to his chest.

'Why did you stop the Bed and Breakfast?' he asked.

'Several reasons,' said Kathleen. 'Me for one. My asthma was getting intolerable. It's really a nervous condition with me. The very thought of summer would bring on an attack. Then there was the Troubles, of course. After '69 people just stopped coming. Now we call this place the last resort.'

'When we were here the place was full of Scotch.'

'Yes and the same ones came back year after year. But after the Troubles started nobody would risk it. I wrote to people telling them that this place was as safe as anywhere in the world, but they never came back. Then Mary got a job teaching when the new school was built.'

'And mother died,' said Mary.

'Oh did she? I never saw her. We just heard her – upstairs.'

'She was very demanding,' said Kathleen, 'and I was in no position to cope with her. It was she really who insisted that we keep the place open. All her life she had a great fear of ending up in the poor-house. She was the one who had the bright idea of extending out the back just before the slump. We're still paying the mortgage.' Mr Maguire set his cup and saucer on the hearth.

'Do you mind if I smoke?' He addressed Mary who turned to her sister.

'Kathleen?'

'I like the smell of pipe-smoke. It's cigarettes I can't stand.' Mr Maguire took out a small straight pipe and a yellow plastic pouch. He filled the pipe as he listened to Kathleen talk about the old days when the house was full of guests. Mary watched him press the tobacco into the bowl with his index finger. When he struck the match he whirled his hand in a little circle to attenuate the flare before holding the match to his pipe. The triangular flame gave little leaps as he held it over the bowl and drew air through it, his lips popping quietly. Throughout the whole operation he continued to nod and say 'hm-hm' to Kathleen's talk.

'You'll just have to take us as we are,' she was saying, 'not being officially open and all that. I'll give you a key and you can come and go as you like.'

'Thank you,' said Mr Maguire striking another match.

'And I ... ke a fry in the morning?'

'... big fry. I wouldn't

think I was on holiday if I didn't. Do you still bake your own wheaten bread?'

'No, my asthma. The flour can sometimes go for it. Let me get you an ashtray,' said Kathleen jumping up. Mr Maguire sat with a tiny bouquet of dead matches between his fingers.

'Did you ever think of selling?'

Kathleen laughed and Mary smiled down into the fire.

'We tried for three years,' said Kathleen. 'Would *you* buy it? It's like trying to sell my asthma. Nobody wants it. The ads were costing us so much that we had to take it off the market.'

When the tea was finished Kathleen showed him up to his room, talking constantly even over her shoulder on the stairs. Mary followed them, her hands tucked into the opposite sleeves of her jacket, like a nun. The bed was stripped to its mattress of blue and white stripes. Mr Maguire set his bag by the window.

'I'll put the electric blanket on to air the bed for you,' said Kathleen.

'Thank you,' he said. 'You get a great view from this window.' Mary stared over his shoulder at the metallic sea. His face in the light was sallow and worn with vertical creases down each side of his mouth and his forehead corrugated into wrinkles as he spoke. He wouldn't win any prizes for his looks but somehow his face suited him. He gave the impression of being an ex-sportsman, wiry and tough, tall enough to have developed a slight stoop of the shoulders. He had enough hair to make her wonder whether or not it was a toupee. If it was, it was a very convincing one. He asked,

'Where's a good place to eat now?'

'The Royal do a nice meal,' said Kathleen.

'The Royal?'

'Is that too expensive?'

'It was in my day.' Kathleen lifted the foot of the bed and eased it out from the wall.

'Try the Croft Kitchen,' she said. 'I think they're still open. What little season there is, is over.' Seeing him hesitate she added, 'It's on High Street opposite what used to be the Amusements.' She stepped out on to the landing and pointed. 'The bathroom is second on your right. The light switch is on the outside.'

'Yes, I remember.'

'I'll just get some bed linen.' Kathleen hurried off down the landing.

'She's excited,' said Mary, her voice lowered. Mr Maguire smiled and nodded. His voice was as quiet as hers.

'On our honeymoon,' he said, 'my wife went to the bathroom . . .'

Mary withdrew her hands from her sleeves and straightened a picture, '... and someone turned out the light on her. She was terrified. She heard a footstep, then the light went out, then breathing. The poor woman sat for half the night in the dark before she had the courage to come out. I was sound asleep, of course.'

'How awful,' said Mary. Kathleen strode in, the fresh bed linen pressed between her arms like a white accordion.

'Right, there's work to be done,' she said dumping them on the bed.

That night even though she felt tired and had gone to bed early Mary could not sleep. She heard Mr Maguire come in at a reasonable hour. Apart from a little throat-clearing he himself was quiet but she heard everything he did – the popping of the wash basin in her own room as he used his, the flush of the toilet from the end of the corridor, the creaking of his bed through the wall as he got into it. It seemed hours before she heard the snap of his bedside light being switched off and she wondered what book it was that kept him reading so late.

She woke several times and each time was wet with perspiration, so much so that she was afraid she had had an accident. She felt like the shamelessly vulgar girl on the calendar which hung above the cash desk in the garage emerging from the waves in a dripping white chemise which concealed nothing. Her condition was becoming worse instead of better. At times in front of her classes she felt as if there was a hole in her head and she was being filled from top to toe, like a hot water bottle. Some months ago Kathleen had become alarmed one day seeing her sister steady herself with her knuckles on the kitchen table, her face red and wet with perspiration.

'What's wrong?'

Mary had simply said that her ovaries were closing down. The inner woman was giving up the ghost, but not without a struggle. She bathed twice a day now – when she got up in the morning and before her evening meal. She refused to go to the doctor because, she said, the condition was normal. The *Home Encyclopaedia of Medicine* told her all she wanted to know. Letters in women's magazines frequently dealt with the subject, in some cases in embarrassing detail. It was a sign of the times when you bought a perfectly middle-of-the-road woman's magazine and were frightened to open the pages because of what you might read; sex mixed in with the knitting patterns; among the recipes, orgasms and homosexuality and God knows what else. She was embarrassed, not on her own behalf, but for the teenagers in her classes. Magazines, like the ones she bought, would inevitably be going into all their homes. Each time her eyes flinched away from reading such an article she blushed for the destruction of her pupils' innocence. As for some of the daily papers now, she wouldn't give them house room.

Mr Maguire cleared his throat and she heard the twang of him turning in his seldom-used bed.

During the last class of the day Mary stood staring, not out, but at the window. On this, the leeward side of the school, the glass was covered with rain droplets which trembled in unison at each spent gust of wind. Behind her a fourth-year class worked quietly at a translation exercise. She was proud of her reputation for having the most disciplined classes in the school. She knew the pupils disliked her for it but it was something they would thank her for in later life. Within the rigid structures she set – woe betide anybody who overstepped the guidelines – she knew they felt safe. Clear orders produced order, indecision produced chaos.

At ten to four she saw Mr Maguire walking out the road past the school with his hands clasped behind his back and his head down into the wind. When she eventually got out of school he was standing smiling at the gate.

'I thought it must be that time,' he said, 'and I was just passing.' He offered to carry her bag but she said that it was light enough. Other days she would have been grateful. They began walking into the fine drizzle.

'What a day that was. Do you have children, Mr Maguire?'

'No, my wife was never a well woman. It would have been too much to ask.' He twisted his mouth making a face of resignation. Again she was struck by the coarseness of his accent. His face relaxed and he smiled.

'Where did all the books come from in your house?' he asked.

'That was my father mostly. He was Headmaster of the local Primary. He was interested in all sorts of things. Nature study, science, history. We were always used to books in the house.'

'You were lucky. I had to do all the work myself. At a very late stage. Imagine sitting your A-levels for the first time at fifty.'

'Is that what you did?'

'I'm afraid so.'

'I admire that.'

Mr Maguire shrugged shyly.

'Not everybody does,' he said. 'My wife used to make fun of me. But she had a very hard time of it. She was in a lot of pain and couldn't understand. I think she was jealous of the time I spent reading. She thought it was a hobby or a pastime or something like that. She couldn't have been further from the truth.' Seeing Mary change her briefcase from her right to her left hand Mr Maguire insisted that he carry it for her. She reluctantly handed it over to him. He continued talking.

'When you find out about real education you can never leave it alone. I don't mean A-levels and things like that – you are just proving something to yourself with them – but books, ideas, feelings. Everything to do with up here.' He tapped his temple. 'And here.' He tapped the middle of his chest. Mary asked,

'What do you like to read then?'

'The classics. Fiction. Good stuff.'

The wind tugged at his hair blowing it into various partings. It was definitely not a toupee.

'I sometimes stop here and walk to the end.' She pointed to the pier, its back arched against the running sea. Occasionally a wave broke over it and spray slapped down on the concrete. Some boys with schoolbags were running the gauntlet along the pier.

'They'll get soaked, or worse,' said Mr Maguire.

'That's nothing. This summer I saw them ride off the end on a bicycle. They had it tied to one of the bollards so's they could pull it up each time. I couldn't watch. It gave me the funniest feeling. I had to go away in the end.'

When they got back to the house Mr Maguire set her briefcase in the hall, nodded to her and climbed the stairs. Mary went to the kitchen and sat on a stool beside the Rayburn drying out as the kettle boiled.

'Where's our guest?' asked Kathleen.

'Upstairs.'

'He's a strange fish. But nice.'

'Yes, you and he certainly seem to get along,' said Mary. Kathleen rolled her eyes to heaven. Mary laughed and said,

'He walks like the Duke of Edinburgh.' She stood up and did an imitation backwards and forwards across the kitchen, her hands joined behind her back, her head forward like a tortoise. Kathleen laughed and said,

'I was making his bed today and do you know what he's reading? Or at least he has it lying on his bedside table.'

'I've no idea.'

'A book of English verse.'

'Why not?'

'It doesn't tally somehow. Him and poetry. And do you know – he's brought a full shoe-polishing kit with him. Brushes, tins, cloths the lot. Mother would have been so pleased.'

'You shouldn't nosey.'

'I couldn't help seeing them. I had to move them out of my way to make the bed.'

'What's wrong with being careful about your appearance?'

'Nothing. But it seems extravagant to bring everything on holiday.' Kathleen heard Mr Maguire's footsteps on the landing and bounded to the kitchen door.

'There's a cup of tea in the pot, Mr Maguire,' she called.

'Thank you, I won't be a minute.'

When he came in Mary smelt soap off his hands as he reached in front of her for his cup. Shaking his hand the day before it had felt hard and crusty, like someone who had laboured all his life.

'Well Mr Maguire,' asked Kathleen. 'How was your day?'

'The rain drove me home,' he smiled. His hair was wet and neatly parted, dark as if he had used hair-oil. 'You see how I call it *home* already. But I suppose home is where you're at.' Kathleen offered him a biscuit but he refused.

'How was your meal in the Croft Kitchen last night?'

'It was closed.'

'Where did you eat then?' Kathleen made her voice sound aghast.

'The café place on the front. It was good. Reasonable too.'

'Eucch, what a place,' she shuddered. 'And all those sauce bottles on the tables. They're encrusted.'

'No, it was fine, really.'

'Look,' said Kathleen firmly. 'We don't eat extravagantly ourselves but you're welcome to join us this evening.'

'Ah now that wouldn't be fair.'

'We're just having minced steak and carrots. It's no bother to set a place for an extra one.' Mr Maguire hesitated. He looked at Mary who was staring into her cup. She raised her eyes to him.

'Why don't you stay?' she said.

'Are you sure it wouldn't be any trouble?'

'Not in the least,' said Kathleen.

'Only on one condition. You must charge me extra.'

'That's settled then,' said Kathleen. 'We can haggle about the price later.'

'It's very kind of you. Both of you.'

Mr Maguire appeared at dinnertime wearing a tie but no jacket. Mary sat opposite him, the tails of hair at her neck still damp from her bath, while Kathleen served and talked.

'What are you doing this evening, Mr Maguire?'

'I'm not sure.'

'Do you play whist?'

'No.' He crushed his potatoes into the gravy of his mince.

'There's a whist drive in aid of church funds in the hall. Guests are very welcome.' She sat down to her own meal.

'I'm sorry,' said Mr Maguire. 'I was never any good at card games. Especially whist where your partner depends on you to play the right card. I played once or twice and at the finish-up my shins were black and blue.'

'I *have* to go,' said Kathleen. 'I'm organizing a table. Mary, will you run me up? I have all those cups and saucers and things.' Mary nodded, her mouth full.

'Can you not drive?' asked Mr Maguire.

'No. I'm too nervous. But Mary is very good, runs me everywhere.' Kathleen took on the responsibility of the silences and when one occurred she talked, mostly to Mr Maguire.

'What is it you do, Mr Maguire?'

'At the moment, nothing. I've just been made redundant. One of the three million.'

'Oh that's too bad.'

'Yes, when I got my redundancy money I said to heck I'll treat myself to a holiday.'

'You were just right,' said Kathleen. 'You can't take it with you.'

'There'll be none of it left to take with me.'

Both sisters smiled. Mr Maguire looked at Mary and she felt obliged to speak.

'What did you work at?'

'In a big warehouse. Spare parts for cars.'

'Oh I see,' said Mary.

'I'd been there for most of my life.'

'Then you know a bit about cars?'

'A bit.'

'It's just that mine is not going properly.'

'What is it?'

'A Fiat.'

'No, I mean what is the problem?'

'It seems to have no power, sluggish.'

'I could have a look at it tomorrow.'

Kathleen interrupted.

'But I thought you were going tomorrow?'

'Would you mind if I stayed the weekend? I have no real reason to rush back.'

'Certainly,' said Kathleen. 'Especially if you can fix the car.'

'Thank you.' Mr Maguire had cleared his plate in a matter of minutes. Kathleen offered him second helpings which he took.

'It's the sea air,' he said. 'Gives you an appetite. This is what I cook mostly for myself because it's easy.' Then he seemed embarrassed. 'I'm sorry. This tastes a hundred times better than my efforts. I just mean that it doesn't take much looking after on the stove.'

'I gather you don't like cooking?'

'No. At home I do a standard menu. The boiled egg. The mince. The fry. When you're on your own food doesn't seem as interesting. I find it hard enough to get through a whole loaf without it going bluemould.' He laughed. 'I eat watching the news with my plate on my knees. Rarely set the table.'

'Is there any chance that you'll get another job?'

'I doubt it. The car trade is in a bad way and it's the only one I know. I'm fifty-six now. Prospects – poor.' He shrugged. Mary looked at his hands. They were big and red, making toys of his knife and fork. The nail of his right-hand thumb was opaque like a hazelnut shell.

Kathleen had baked an apple tart for the guest and they had it with cream. Mr Maguire took a second portion after a little coaxing.

'I don't really want a job,' he said. 'Now I'll have the time to do what I want to do.'

'And what's that?'

'Read. Dig my plot. I'm going to do this Open University thing. On the television. I've just enrolled but it doesn't start until next January. I paid the fees out of the redundancy as well.'

'You make the dole sound like a good thing.'

'I've always been keen. If there's a WEA class on the go, I'm your man.'

'What have you done up until now?'

'God save us,' said Mr Maguire laughing and trying to recall.

'Spanish, English, Philosophy – there was a Botany year but I couldn't make head nor tail of it. Anything and everything. I'm a dabbler.'

Kathleen got out of the car at the church hall balancing a cardboard box full of trembling cups. She slammed the door with her heel.

'Hey just you be careful with that Mr Maguire, Mary,' she said through the driver's window.

'He's a bit down-market for me, dear.' Mary laughed. 'Besides it's you he fancies.'

'Will you pick me up?'

Mary nodded.

On her way back she was irritated again by the lack of energy in the engine. On the hill of High Street it seemed to have barely sufficient power to pull her up. She thought about Mr Maguire.

'Thank God it's Friday,' she said aloud.

She had kicked off her shoes and was just sitting down to look in the evening paper what was on television when there was a quiet rap on the door. Mr Maguire stood there with a light bulb in his hand. She smelt tobacco smoke off him.

'I'm sorry to trouble you,' he said, 'but my reading light has gone and I wondered if you had a spare one?' Mary, in stockinged feet climbed on to a stool and produced a new 60-watt bulb from a high cupboard. She exchanged bulbs with him and for some reason felt foolish. He stood for a moment with the cardboard package in his hands.

'Is it raining?' he asked.

'No, not now.'

He moved the piece of card that held the bulb in place against the corrugations of the package, rippling it.

'Are you busy this evening?' he asked. Mary hesitated.

'No.'

'Would you like to go somewhere – for a drink perhaps?'

'I don't like going into pubs.'

'The hotel – we could go to the Royal, just for a while. An orange juice, if you like.' Mary was now holding the dead bulb by its tiny pins between her finger and her thumb. She swung it backwards and forwards.

'It's Friday,' she said. 'Why not?' Mr Maguire smiled.

'In about half an hour then?'

'Yes.'

He turned quickly to the stairs holding up the new bulb in a gesture of thanks. For a ridiculous moment she expected it to light as if he was some kind of statue.

She closed the door and out of habit, before she threw the used bulb in the waste-paper basket, she shook it close to her ear. There was no tingling sound. She switched off the standard lamp and removed the hot bulb with a serviette. Mr Maguire's bulb lit when she switched it on.

Mary washed herself and changed her clothes again even though she had done the same thing two hours before. She dabbed a little perfume behind her ears and put on some lipstick which she normally didn't wear. In the hotel lounge after the first sip of her sherry she took a tissue from her handbag and wiped the red crescent stain of her lower lip from the rim of the glass. Mr Maguire was drinking Guinness. She sat on the edge of her seat, her shoulders back, her head regal. Her mother had always talked about 'bearing'. How she had detested that woman's constant chivvying. One day as they walked to church, the two girls in front, the mother and father behind, she had prodded Mary between the shoulder blades with the point of her umbrella.

'Don't slouch, Mary,' she had said, 'if you want to keep your bosoms separate.' She could still feel the ferrule to this very day and the spitting hatred it had caused her. And yet now, without being told, she did everything her mother had asked her.

'Relax,' said Mr Maguire.

'I'm not used to being in places like this.'

'Take off your coat.' He stood like a gentleman to take it from her and went to hang it on a rack at the far side of the lounge. Mary sat with her handbag on the seat beside her. The place was plush and had been redecorated since she had last been in. Musak took away from the early evening hush of the place.

'I've only been here at weddings,' she said when he came back.

'It's a nice place.'

'The word will be out on Monday at school that Miss Bradley was seen boozing with a man.' Mr Maguire laughed.

'What do you teach?'

'German and a little French.'

'Have you ever been to Germany?'

'No, but I taught for a year in a German-speaking part of Switzerland. In a beautiful place called Kandersteg.'

'I've never been abroad. Never in anything bigger than a rowing boat. And as for planes – if you ever hear of me being killed in a plane crash you'll know it fell on me.' Mary laughed and took another sip of her sherry.

'It was up in the mountains. A typical Swiss village with cuckoo-clock houses. Green grass and flowers at your feet and snow when you looked up. And the children were so well behaved. It was a dream to teach there.'

Mr Maguire took out his pipe and stirred its bowl with the bottom end of a match, then knocked the black tobacco into the ashtray. She thought there was something comfortable about this ritual of emptying and filling and lighting. He did it without paying the slightest attention. By his face and the tilt of his head he was absorbed in listening to her.

'It was like a holiday really,' she said. 'It's funny how you remember the good things so vividly.'

'Maybe it's because there's so few of them,' he said. 'I remember my honeymoon as if it was yesterday.'

'Ah but that's different. I'm talking about holidays. Sunshine, noises and smells you're not used to.'

'No that's what I mean. I remember this town, your house. We sat by the Rayburn and talked to the wee small hours. It was a cold summer.'

'We did?'

'Well, once, maybe twice. And then one night I remember you were going to a dance and you came into the kitchen. You were in your stocking feet frantically looking for your shoes. You left a wake of scent behind you.' Mary laughed covering her mouth with her hand. Mr Maguire drew a large ring around himself with his arms. 'You were out to here with petticoats. The dress was white with wee green flecks in it.'

'That's right, that's right,' Mary interrupted. 'I remember that one. Parsley Sauce we used to call it. Those were the days when you had so few dresses you gave them names.' She rolled her eyes to heaven. It was embarrassing – it was as if this man had produced a sheaf of old photographs of her. 'Isn't it awful that I remember the dress but I've no recollection whatsoever of you.' Suddenly her face straightened in mock disapproval. 'And you noticed all this on your honeymoon?'

'You have no control over what you notice.'

'And where was your wife when you were sitting talking to me – to the wee small hours?' It was as if she was wagging her finger at him.

'She was ill even then. She always went to bed early. I'm a night owl myself.'

'Oh dear me,' she said. 'What a thing to remember – old Parsley Sauce.' Mr Maguire bought more drinks and Mary began to feel relaxed and warm.

'This is nice,' she said. 'I'm glad I came.'

Some ex-pupils of hers came in and sat at the bar. They nodded and smirked towards the corner where she sat.

Mr Maguire asked her about what books she read and she told him that she was an escapist reader. Four or five library books a week she got through. Anything, just so long as it did not make too many demands on her. Kathleen was different – she went in for the more heavy-weight stuff. And of course nothing which would disturb. None of that embarrassing nonsense. It was hard to avoid it nowadays. Library books should have warnings on the covers – be graded like films.

Mr Maguire said that he was the opposite. Unless a book was making him puzzle and think he would throw it away. He thought he had read more first chapters than anybody else in the world. With regard to the embarrassing stuff, if it was not too explicit he could accept it. It was a part of life the same as any other.

Mary refused a third sherry saying that her head was already light, but she insisted on buying Mr Maguire another bottle of Guinness, provided he wanted it. After all, he was on the dole and she was working. When she returned with the poured glass Mr Maguire said,

'Books should not be a means of escape.'

'Why not? We're surrounded by depressing things. Bombs and killings, rapes and God knows what. Who wants to read about them? When I read I prefer to be transported.' Suddenly she put her hand over her mouth in horror. 'Kathleen!' she said. 'I promised to pick up Kathleen. What time is it?'

'Twenty past.'

'She'll kill me.' Already she was on her feet. She hesitated long enough to watch Mr Maguire drain his Guinness, his adam's apple pumping slowly.

'Are you all right for driving?'

He smiled and nodded.

All the lights were out in the church hall and Kathleen was pacing up and down in the porchway out of the rain. Mr Maguire carried her box of cups for her as Mary apologized for being so late. For once Kathleen was quiet. The only sound coming from the back seat of the car was the whine of her inhaler. In the house she slammed doors when she got the chance.

'There are some left-over sandwiches there, if you want them,' she said. To make up for letting Kathleen stand twenty minutes in the cold Mary made the tea. She set out the whist sandwiches, twisted triangles of egg and onion, meat paste, tomato which had seeped through making the bread feel wet. She dropped a spoon twice and giggled. She felt very silly and likeable but was aware of herself hurrying to get back to the other room where Kathleen and Mr Maguire were alone.

The next morning Mary slept late – it was almost a quarter past ten – and was wakened by sunshine slanting through an opening in the curtains and by the constant revving of an engine. She looked out and saw Mr Maguire in a navy boiler-suit beneath the open bonnet of her car, tinkering. Before going downstairs in her dressing gown she freshened up and made herself – apart from the heavy sleep-puffed eyes – look presentable. It was just as well because Mr Maguire came in, his oily hands aloft and washed at the kitchen sink. Kathleen, also in a dressing gown, offered him a cup of tea from the pot.

'I thought oil was difficult to get off,' she said.

'Not if you use a barrier cream before you start.' Mr Maguire dried each finger carefully on the roller towel which hung on the back of the kitchen door.

'And how is the car?' asked Mary.

'I think you should see a big improvement. When did you last have it serviced?'

'Goodness,' said Mary. 'I can't remember. Really.'

'I reset your points, put in three new plugs and changed the oil. The carburettor needed . . .'

'I know nothing about it. You might as well be talking Double Dutch.' Mr Maguire nodded his head in disbelief and sat down at the table laughing.

'What do I owe you?'

'Not a thing. I carry a spare set of plugs. And my time's my own.'

'But that's not fair.'

'Pay me for the oil and we'll call it quits. I went down to the garage for it when you were still snoring.' Mary got her purse and gave him the money which he took with some embarrassment and pushed it into the top pocket of his boiler-suit.

'You look very smart,' said Kathleen, nodding to his outfit.

'I always carry this in the boot. I've been caught out before, changing a wheel on a wet night and me wearing the good suit.'

'But it's so clean.'

Mr Maguire nodded and turned to Mary.

'Would you like to try her out?' For a moment Mary didn't know what he was talking about.

'Oh yes. Let me get dressed first. Kathleen? Do you want to come for a run? It looks a nice day.'

'No, I've things to do.' She said it with an echo of the previous night's bitterness still in her voice.

'Very well, suit yourself.'

They drove out towards Spanish Point. Mary was delighted with the change in the car – it even sounded different. She said so to Mr Maguire, now restored to his casual wear. She herself wore trousers – a thing she never did on teaching days. Mr Maguire said,

'The thing that really fascinated me about this wreck was the ring they found. Have you heard about it?'

'I'm not sure.'

'They brought up a gold ring from the bottom and it had an inscription round the inside. *No tengo mas que dar te*.' With his Belfast accent his attempt at pronunciation was comical. Mary smiled.

'More Double Dutch.'

'It's Spanish. It means "I have nothing more to give thee".'

'That's nice.' She changed down through the gears as they came up behind a tractor on a bend.

'I thought it was very moving to see it after all those years. What I wondered was this. Was he taking it back as a present for a loved one in Spain or had somebody given it to him as he sailed away with the Armada? It makes a big difference.'

'Yes, I suppose it does.' Mary, now on a straight stretch of road, indicated and passed the tractor. She gave a little wave over her shoulder.

'That's Jim McLelland,' she said.

They walked awkwardly on a beach of apple-sized stones hearing them clunk hollowly beneath their feet. Mary felt at a loss because she could not walk properly. She had to extend her arms, like a tightrope walker for balance and once or twice almost had to clutch at Mr Maguire's arm.

'This is pointless,' she said. They halted and looked across at Spanish Point. The sun was warm for the time of year and the wind had all but disappeared. Mary sat on a rock and Mr Maguire standing beside her pulled out his pipe. Now that the rumble of the stones had stopped it was very quiet. For a while neither person spoke. To break the silence Mary asked,

'Have the Troubles touched you where you live in Belfast?'

'A bit,' he said. 'Living alone it's not so bad. Most of the worry people go through is about their nearest and dearest – what'll happen to them.' He said that he had nobody to worry about, apart from himself, and that made it easier. Again the conversation paused.

'Mary.' Hearing him use her name for the first time she looked up startled.

'Yes?'

'You're a remarkable woman,' he said. 'I told you that I came here on holiday to see this place.' He nodded to the black rocks jutting out into the sea. 'That's not the whole truth.' Mary began to feel frightened, alone on the beach with this man whom she hardly knew. She picked up a stone and moved it from hand to hand. It was the tone of his voice that scared her. He was weighing his words, not looking at her.

'I had a memory of this town that was sacred in a way. And over the last couple of days I realize that it is partly your fault – I don't mean fault. I mean that you're part of what's good about it.' Still he didn't look at her but continued to stare out to sea. He had not lit his pipe. Mary could think of nothing, afraid of what he would say next.

'I had forgotten about you, but not completely. Can you imagine how surprised I was when I found you were still here?'

'I've no idea.' She couldn't prevent her voice straying into sarcasm. But he seemed not to notice. She threw the stone with a clatter at her feet, stood up and rubbed her hands together to clean them.

'I think we'd best be getting back,' she said. Mr Maguire looked at her and struck a match on the rock she'd been sitting on. He stood lighting his pipe as Mary made her way towards the car. When he caught up with her he said,

'I'm sorry. I hope I haven't overstepped the mark.'

'I'm not sure what you mean.'

'This past few days have been very real for me. You turn out to be ...' he paused, 'better than I remembered. You have a kind of calm which I envy. A stillness inside.' Mary smiled at him and walked round to the driver's door. Mr Maguire knocked out his pipe on his heel and got into the passenger seat.

'You don't know me at all,' she said, 'if you think I'm calm and still. I'm shaking like a leaf with the kind of things you're saying.'

'I'll say just one more thing – now that I've started – and that'll be the end of it. I'd like you to think about the idea of marrying me.' She turned to him, her eyes wide and her mouth dropping open. She laughed.

'Are you serious?' Mr Maguire smiled slightly as he stared at her, his brow creased with wrinkles.

'Yes, I am.'

'I don't even know your first name.'

'Anthony.'

'You don't look like an Anthony, if you don't mind me saying so.'

'You don't have to say anything. All I want you to do is to give it some thought.' Mary turned on the engine, indicated left and did a U-turn to the right but stalled midway. She tried to switch on the engine again.

'What have you done to this machine?' she said.

'Would you like me to drive?'

Mary agreed and he drove her home in the most embarrassing silence she had ever known.

Mr Maguire climbed the stairs. Mary went straight to the kitchen where she heard Kathleen singing.

'Well?' said Kathleen. 'Big improvement?' Mary sat down on the stool by the Rayburn. She said,

'Make me a cup of tea. I need it badly.'

'What's wrong? Did it break down?' Mary began to laugh.

'You'll never believe this.' Her sister turned from filling the kettle. 'But I've just been proposed to.'

'What? Who?' Her voice was a screech. Mary hushed her and rolled her eyes to the ceiling as Mr Maguire closed a door upstairs. Then they both laughed. 'No, I don't believe you. You'd find out then, if it was a real toupee or not.'

'It's not funny,' said Mary still laughing. 'I was there.'

'What did you tell him?'

'I said I'd think about it.'

As Kathleen made the tea her shoulders shook.

'You'd end up keeping the shine on his wee shoes. And the crease in his boiler-suit. Mother would be pleased.' She wiped her eyes and gave her sister a cup.

'You're not seriously thinking about it?'

'No, but . . .'

'But, what?'

'It's just that I've never really been asked.'

'You have so. Twice. You told me so.'

'But they were ludicrous.'

'And this one isn't?'

'There's something gentlemanly about him.'

'A gentleman of leisure. He's on the dole, Mary.' Kathleen grinned again. 'Did he go down on one knee?'

'Don't be silly.'

Later that afternoon when the laughter had worn off and Mr Maguire had gone for a walk Kathleen said,

'And what would become of me?'

'For goodness' sake Kathleen, I only said I would consider it.'

'I don't think I'd be able to manage on my own. Financially.'

'Kathleen! Will you excuse me. I'd like to make up my own mind on this one.'

Mary went to her bedroom and sat looking at herself in the dressing-table mirror. A hot flush came over her and she watched her face redden, like an adolescent blushing. She flinched at the thought of a kiss from Mr Maguire. And yet he would make a good companion. Eccentric, yes – but basically a good man. In so far as she knew him. Pinpoints of sweat gleamed on her forehead and on her upper lip. She pulled a tissue from the box on the dressing table and dabbed herself dry, then she lay down on the bed. Perhaps she should stall him. Write letters for a period. That way things would not be complicated by his physical presence. By that time, with any luck, these fits would have passed and she would have returned to normality. Stall him. That was the answer. He would enjoy writing to her. It would give him a chance to quote poetry. For some reason Kandersteg came into her mind and with a little thrill she thought of going there on her honeymoon. In July just as soon as the school holidays started. She would have to do all the translation for Mr Maguire. They could call and see if Herr Hauptmann was still alive and they could relive their days at the school while poor Mr Maguire would have to stare out the window at the beautiful view. The grey clouds of mist that moved against the almost black of the forests. The cleanness, the tidiness of their streets, the precision with which trains came and went, not to the minute, but to the second. Herr Hauptmann's hazel-coloured eyes as he listened to her.

At tea Kathleen, activated by nervousness, talked non-stop. She served chops, potatoes and cauliflower cheese. Her monologue was a labyrinth of ballet, the Cuban crisis, sore knees and asthma. What was the aside of one sentence became the main subject of the next and it, in its turn, sprouted another aside. And so it went on until she left the room to make the coffee. Mr Maguire tried to remove a shred of meat from between his teeth delicately with the nail of his little finger. He smiled across the silence at Mary, nodding his head, as if it had become a reflex to the torrent of Kathleen's talk and one that he could not stop even when she had left the room. Mary understood and smiled back. Mr Maguire whispered,

'Kathleen's problem is that she hasn't heard of the paragraph.' Mary nodded in agreement. They could hear the distant rattle of cups and Kathleen humming. Mr Maguire said that he would like to settle his bill as he would be leaving first thing after Mass in the morning when the roads would be relatively traffic free. Mary said,

'It might be nice if we walked to the hotel later. I'd like to make my position clear.'

'Yes that would help.'

'About eight?'

Mr Maguire nodded just as Kathleen pushed the door open with her foot and came in bearing a tray of coffee things.

After Mr Maguire had excused himself and gone to his room Mary said to her sister,

'I'm going for a walk with him later.'

'It makes no difference to me. I have to go up to the church to fix up the flowers.'

'Oh that's right. It's Saturday.' Kathleen began to stack the cups on to the tray with a snatching movement of one hand. The other she held against her chest.

'Have you made up your mind how you're going to tell him?'

'I'm not sure,' said Mary. 'I'm not even sure *what* I'm going to tell him.'

'Don't allow me to influence you one way or the other. You can do whatever you like. All I hope is that you won't do something you will regret for the rest of your life. And if you go traipsing off with him I'll need some help with the mortgage.'

'There's no question of that.' Mary was aware that her voice had risen. 'You can be sure that I'll be sensible about it. If I've waited this long . . .' She didn't finish. Kathleen picked up the tray. Her mouth wavered and turned down at the corners. She set the tray back on the table with a crash and burst into tears. She sat shuddering with her face in her hands.

'What's wrong?' Mary put her hand on her sister's shoulder. When Kathleen was able to control her voice she said,

'I'm scared.' Then with the index finger of each hand she wiped the tears from her cheeks, got up and carried the tray out to the kitchen.

At precisely eight o'clock they both left their rooms. Mr Maguire his shoes burnished, wearing a tie and jacket stood waiting for her. On the street again he walked like the Duke of Edinburgh, one hand holding the other by the wrist behind his back. The fine day had kept up, the night was windless and at intervals between the glare of the street lights they could see stars. Mary was conscious of her high heels clicking on the granite paving stones and was relieved when she came to the softer tarmacadam footpath where she could walk with more dignity. Mr Maguire cleared his throat and asked,

'Well, did you think about what . . . ?'

'Yes, but don't talk about it now. Talk about something else.' Mr Maguire nodded in agreement and looked up at the sky as if for inspiration.

'What is it that makes your life worthwhile?'

'What a strange question. I don't know,' she laughed nervously and tried to give an answer. 'I suppose I help children to learn something. Give them the rudiments of another language. And I help Kathleen who cannot work . . .'

'I don't mean what is worthwhile to others. But to yourself.'

'Sometimes, Mr Maguire, you say the oddest things. I'm sorry I don't see the difference.'

'Take it from another angle. What makes you really angry?' She felt her shoulder brush against his as they walked.

'The kind of thing that's been going on in this country. Killings, bombings . . .'

'If you were to give one good reason to stop someone blowing your head off tonight, what would it be?'

'I've jotters to correct for Monday.' Mr Maguire laughed. 'Well there's that,' Mary went on, 'and children and love and Kathleen and ...'

'And what?'

'And I've dresses that I've only worn once or twice. And the sea. And the occasional laugh in the staff room. And apple crumble. Just everything.'

'You would be part of the reason I would give.'

There was a long pause and Mary said,

'Thank you. That's very nice of you to say so. But as I say, I'd prefer to wait until we were settled inside before we have our little talk.' Mr Maguire shrugged and smiled. Mary veered off to look in the shop window of Madge's Fashions which was still lit up. There was a single old-fashioned window model with painted on brown hair instead of a wig and white flakes where the paint had chipped off, particularly at the red fingernails.

'They've changed the dress since Friday,' said Mary. 'I like that one better.' She joined Mr Maguire in the middle of the pavement still looking back over her shoulder.

They sat at the same table as last night and Mr Maguire bought the same drinks.

'They'll be calling me a regular next,' said Mary as Mr Maguire slid into the seat beside her. She took a careful sip from the surface of the brimming glass so that the next time she lifted it, it would not spill. They replaced their glasses simultaneously.

'Well now ...' said Mary, 'I think ... First of all let me say that I find it extremely difficult to talk in a situation like this. I'm out of my depth.' She tried not to sound like she was introducing a lesson, but what she said was full of considered pauses. She spoke as quietly as she could, yet distinctly. Mr Maguire distracted her from what she was about to say by pulling out his pipe and blowing through it to make sure it was clear. 'You are an interesting man, good – as far as I know you – but these are not reasons,' she paused yet again, 'for anybody to get married. It has happened so quickly that there is an element of foolishness in it. And that's not me.'

'It's me,' said Mr Maguire laughing.

'There are so many things. I'm not a free agent. Kathleen has got to be considered.'

'She can fairly talk.'

'Yes, sometimes it's like living with the radio on. She never expects an answer.'

'Do you love her?'

'I suppose I must. When you live with someone day in, day out the trivial things become the most important.' She sipped her sherry and felt the glass tremble between her fingertips. 'And there are other things which frighten me. I don't think I'm that sort of person.' Mr Maguire looked at her but she was unable to hold his eye and her gaze returned to her sherry glass.

'My wife was in poor health for many, many years – so that aspect of it should not worry you. I am in the habit of – not. I would respect your wishes. Although I miss someone at my back now when I fall asleep.' Mary thought of herself slippery with sweat lying awake making sure to keep centimetres between herself and Mr Maguire's slow breathing body.

'I can't believe this is happening to me.' She laughed and turned to face him with her hands joined firmly in her lap. 'My answer is – in the kindest possible way – no. But why don't you write to me? Why don't you come back and stay with us for longer next year? Writing would be a way of getting to know each other.'

'Your answer is no – for now?'

'Yes.'

'But there's a definite maybe in there somewhere?'

'More like a possible perhaps not,' said Mary. 'I mean it's ridiculous at our age.'

'I don't see why. Could I come up at Christmas? Or Easter?' She thought of herself and Kathleen in new dresses, full of turkey and sprouts and mince pies, dozing in armchairs and watching television for most of the day. The Christmas programmes were always the best of the year.

'No. Not Christmas.'

'Easter then?'

'Write to me and we'll see.'

Mr Maguire smiled and shrugged as if he had lost a bet.

'You've kind of taken the wind out of my sails,' he said.

The next morning when she got up Mr Maguire had gone. Kathleen had called him early and given him his breakfast. When he had paid his bill she deducted a fair amount for the servicing of the car.

After Mass, surrounded by the reality of the Sunday papers, Mary thought how silly the whole thing had been. The more she thought about the encounter the more distasteful it became. She resolved to answer his first letter out of politeness but, she said firmly to herself, that would be the finish of it.

On the Monday she was feeling down and allowed herself the luxury of a lesson, taught to four different levels throughout the day, in which she talked about Kandersteg, its cuckoo-clock houses and the good Herr Hauptmann.

J. New

The Game at Ghost Beach

J. NEW was born in 1952 in South Shields. He now lives in Oxfordshire, where he has completed a book, *100 Stories* – from which 'The Game at Ghost Beach' is taken – and a set of fifty paintings.

Where once courting couples by night in the dunebeds, and by day picnicking families, for sport, and where the off-work businessman would run his dog each morning, was now only the ghost of a beach, that had been dozed under by the council who wanted to put the town's waste there, that was as close to the edge as they could get it without it all tumbling over. Now dogs alone, and the occasional dirty boys, ran, playing their games on that infected ground.

Also gulls, perpetually, grey, shifting, picking the dump over, that would rise with the quietest screams to one another when you approached, to settle again at their PICK when you had passed them by, like ghosts.

Here youngsters have their game, for example, little Ray and his friend Triv(or).

The first day there they said, come-on, let us go and find a wheel, and scoured the area together, scanning here and there, until they found a bicycle's, that was soon done on this dumping-ground, where there were many. They took it to a flat rock as their table, that stood on a platform of excess earth, bulldozed and packed down, moraine-like, on a shelf overlooking the sea. They clattered the spokes with sticks, wheeled it, threw it at each other, and threw it away. Next morning they wanted a wheel again and Ray said, let us see who can find one first, I think I'll be able to find one before you, I bet, monkey-face. Then ran like hell until Triv picked up a tyre at almost the same moment that Ray pulled some cog (townhall-clock style) free from its matrix of mud. They held them up and waved them at each other across the intervening waste, then Ray, who was nearest to it, shouted the first one back to the rock! And he won, just, on that occasion. Triv said, you call that a wheel? What are all those teeth doing around the edge? And Ray said, so? What do you think yours is? It is only a *rim*, if you ask me. Then they threw them away and said see who finds a bottle first (and be first back with it to the rock). Which was an easy one too. Triv found a perfume-spray bulb (frosted 'crystal') and Ray a bottle of haig, then running back Ray was nearest again, but when Triv was within throwing distance, as he judged, he threw the bulb on to the rock before Ray could get there, where it broke into a million pieces. That doesn't count, they argued the toss. Triv says, what's yours, a whisky? I would like to bet some old tramp's been at it. I bet some old tramp's had a piss in it. Ha ha. I am lucky I havint touched it! Now let's what? And so they went on, and on the next day too.

On the day after that Triv suggested that instead of them both looking for the same kind of thing, he would give Ray a particular thing to have to get, and Ray could give him a different particular thing to have to get, like a task, to see who could give his opponent the hardest task. Triv said, a lamp, Ray said, a television, or just the tube would do, to be fair. And Triv won that round. Then Ray said I think it would be the best plan easily if I made you a list of things to get and you made me one, because then we wouldn't have to keep coming back, and stopping and starting, and the one with his whole list back first to the rock would be the winner. So I have to make you a different list? Yes. But with the same number of things? That's right. And they chose a list of five-each for the first one.

Ray's First Five:	Triv's First Five:
radio	bone
aerial	bulb (light)
harpic	brush
a crockery (any)	basket (fruit)
a tableware (somesort)	ball

Triv said all the one's you've give me start with the same letter. Hat's 'b' for 'bastard' (snort) said Ray-mund, then they set off finding, which lasted them the whole morning until Triv, who had found all his except 'bone', got a sheepscheek from an old boiled head, and put it with all the other things on his side of the rock and called Ray in, who came unwillingly, having neither an aerial nor a harpic.

When they tried lists of ten objects it took too long, and they had to go home when it grew dark without either of them finishing. Or they could have picked easier (more likely) objects for long lists, and harder (more scarce) for short ones, in a proportional manner, which would have made the long lists more of a race, and the short ones more of a test. But this would not have been worth the effort. They did not think much of this idea. It was not something that it appealed to them to do. It was too much trouble. Then Ray said look. I have got a better play. When I give you a list of things to get, you have to get them in the same order that they are given in the list. In the same order? In the same order. Get it?

Ray's Next Five:	Triv's Next Five:
1. soldier	1. cap
2. plane	2. tie
3. umbrella	3. watch
4. pistol	4. belt
5. sword	5. shoe

Ray found an umbrella as soon as he started, and hid it under a 'rubble', but its handle stuck out and he thought that if Triv saw it on his travels he would take it away and hide it somewhere else. So he dug it out of the rubble and took it, close to his jumper, over to a roll of carpet, and pushed it between these damp folds. But Triv had been keeping his eye out, and all Ray's dithering caught his attention so as soon as the coast was clear Triv ran to where he had seen him, found the carpet, found the umbrella inside it, and threw it into the high weeds growing at the base of the cliff which overlooked their playing-ground. So Ray might have done better to have left it alone in the first place, and pretended not to have seen it, and have come back for it later. This is the beauty of order. He was able to hide three shoes without being seen, though, foxing Triv in turn, and found another umbrella shortly after Triv's raid on his cache, then (4) and (5) were easily brought in, and he won that game.

It wasn't the shoes, there's plenty. But I couldn't find a bastard watch anywhere. That is not my fault Ray said. No, it isn't, but make yr mind up I'm going to give you one of the cunts next time, because it's impossible, I have never even *seen* one down here, watches aren't the kind of thing people throw away, they keep them in their drawers! But are we supposed to only put easy things on, because it would get too easy? And so on. Until they made a rule that you were allowed to put any object on the list, as long as you had seen at least one on the dump before. Then they played on, prowling, keeping sharp, tracking, on the lookout, planning, hiding, and performing the task to rights.

You never knew what you might find in the course of a game. One morning Ray saw a refrigerator on the old gun-emplacement up at the quiet end of the cliffs, and when he opened the door there was a cat inside on a shelf, sticking, and on the next shelf up two fieldmice, and their nest in the freezer compartment, and everything in the nest dead too, simply.

Another day they were looking for black goods and found a school blackboard that the rain had warped almost to a hoop. Piss on it, they said. It is the ol' Nipp's blackboard.

At the end of every game, all the objects collected had to be thrown away, this was their rule, and not put back on the dump where someone unscrupulous, like Ray, or prone to dishonesty, like Triv, could take them, hide them, and imitation-find them in the course of some future game. If the tide was out they carried their finds over the wet rocks to the middle region and left them in pools, or weighed down with stones if they might float. But if the tide was in they carried them to a point where the cliff shelved, cutting off the bay. They climbed to the end of the shelf and threw the objects into the sea.

One late afternoon with an armchair, outsprung and ripped, that it took them an hour to manoeuvre up the rocks and along the worn-out snatches of path on to the shelf, then dropped this bulk into the water which took it out a few yards, on the turn, then held it rocking while Ray and Triv pelted it with small stones, while it grew heavy, darker, sinking, until only one corner with a castor sticking out, and that went down too. So they were late home. But this was not their game, this was a practice.

Seeking waste, Triv found a cistern overgrown in the banked nettles beneath the cliff, broken-in, furred inside, and stinking of cod. He ill never get that he thought, and put it as number two on Ray's next list: a tank. But was surprised when they played, and Ray ran twice to the rock, so he says not so quick! What have you got? Ray had a toy tank (Chieftain). Triv said, I didn't say we could use *models*. It's not right if we are going to start using *models*. I didn't mean *that*. But Ray, genuine, asked him what he was talking about, as if: you expect me to find a real tank? I am to drive back in it or what? Triv still smarted though. It was not even out-smarted, only a mixup.

That night Ray-mund dreamed he looked for a porcupine along the beach and, like Robinson Crusoe, stranded, and he found a solitary page from a storybook lying on the sand, and when he picked it up and read it it seemed to contain the word 'porcupine', but he could not be sure because this particular word moved, rattling its letters so they could not be made out. It scuttled up the page, line over line, and when it reached the top and he thought he had it cornered, it slipped over on to the other side, and he dropped the page quick not wanting to get its 'darts' or 'pricks' in his hand.

Next day Triv, to be clever, brought a big-store catalogue he had taken from his mother, and when Ray gave him his list he leafed through the catalogue until he found a picture of the required item, tore it out, and put it on the rock. Even-stevens fuckface said Ray, pulled the book off him, and started to read his list out from the index. Then they fell out fighting. I ill take yr head off, wld see you do it, fairy-boy, and so forth.

After this Ray played alone. He had three different lists. When he played one of them he timed himself, and next day either played a different list, and compared times, or played the same list to beat his best time. After a month of this he made a new set of three lists and kept their times separately, comparing them against each other, but never against the lists in the first set. The objects in each list were different to those in any other list. Thus, in time, each set and each list came to have its own character, its tricky numbers, its standard sequences, and yet because the contents of the dump were constantly changing, under decay and daily delivery, these characters themselves would shift at times, the standard object become tricky for a couple of weeks in summer, say, or what was hard to find would become suddenly commonplace as some new craze swept the town above. And if he ever found the play becoming too regular, he would try collecting the lists in reverse order, to see how their characters could be transformed.

Of course he found things that were never on any list. One day a blackback gull, dead, and picked it up to test the weight and the disturbance caused a drop of little white things to fall from its breast. Or again a maroon squid that the tide had left behind, over a metre long, that it could not be known if it was alive or dead, and that he was not prepared to touch.

One day looking for chains he found a pocket radio that was no bigger than his hand, and there must have been some JUICE left in its batteries because when he knocked it it hissed at him, like a small beast, and after tuning on the dial started to sing, at the top of its voice as it seemed on that quiet ground, oh why did you ever go away? Ba-by? Oh why did you everever go away, the waves seem to whisper goodbye. Tears fill my eyes. The waves seem to whisper goodbye. Tears fill my eyes. The waves seem to whisper. And although it was not near the end of his game, he carried the radio straight up on to the shelf and threw it, that was still singing, into the sea. Half-expecting steam and bubbles where it went in, but that sank like a stone, clearly.

Julia O'Faolain

The Irish Signorina

JULIA O'FAOLAIN, daughter of Sean, lived for a number of years in Florence. This extract is the first chapter of her forthcoming novel and eighth book of fiction, *The Irish Signorina*.

*T*he car turned in through iron gates and there was the villa. *'Bella?'* The chauffeur parked before the pale, apricot façade. Anne agreed. *'Bella, si!'*

The stucco was luminous. Her vision blurred, then steadied and some tossed sequins became a fountain familiar from a snapshot in which her mother was sitting on its rim. There too the sun had been dazzling and the bronze dolphin spouting the water jet seemed ready to melt in its blaze. Mummy, Anne thought, looked happier in that snap than in all the years they had known each other. She had been nineteen. Today the dolphin looked less agile. Its outline had thickened under layers of water weed.

'Signorina.'

A man in livery was picking up Anne's luggage. The air was honey-coloured. Holes seemed to be pierced in it by the movement of micro-scopic gnats.

He waved her through a loggia, a hall and into a room so dark that she hesitated to follow and stood peering.

'La Signorina Ryan,' she heard him announce. Ree-ann was how he said it. 'La Signorina Anne Ree-ann.'

She caught smells of fruit and shut-in humanity. Then a voice answered in Italian, telling him to open the shutters. Light knifed in through the gloom revealing about twenty people sitting upright on chairs and sofas. All were old, wore black and stared unnervingly at Anne.

She smiled, but no one smiled back. One or two blinked – blinded by the inrush of light and part of her panicked to think it could be she who was somehow appalling them. She tried to guess which was the Marchesa but nobody here resembled her pictures in Mummy's old album. Well, twenty-four years was a long time – and, besides, the black of their clothes extinguished all difference in the bundles confronting her. Slowly, one of these stirred, attempted to heave its bulk from a sofa, then abandoned the effort with an acquiescent wheeze.

'Anne!' cried the bundle in confident English. 'How like your mother you look! Come in. Come over. I'm Niccolosa – the Marchesa Cavalcanti.'

Anne crossed the room while the man servant adjusted the shutters so that the light was filtered through slats. Beneath some surface scratchiness, the Marchesa's embrace was like an encounter with a duvet. She clutched Anne's wrist and scrutinized her face. Her own was cone-shaped, thrusting, shrewd. She was perhaps seventy or seventy-five.

'Your mother!' she marvelled. 'Yes.' But went on staring.

Tangible as dust motes, memory eddied through the room. The gathering, it was explained, was a memorial for the Marchesa's daughter, Flavia, whom Anne's mother had chaperoned when both girls were the age Anne was now.

'Twenty-five years ago, was it?'

'Nearly, oh yes, nearly!'

Heads nodded, and Anne, working round the circle, shook hands with relatives of the dead Flavia whom she had never met. Several detained her and murmured. They could have been praying. The Marchesa had clearly failed to foresee the effect of bringing a girl in a pink dress into this black-garbed company. Anne could have been Flavia risen and grown young. The ladies clicked their tongues at the notion. Wasn't she, though, someone wondered, more like Flavia's friend? *E già!* The little Irish girl! But this was her daughter! The Irish girl's? Well! And how, Anne was asked, was her mother? Dead too? Ai! The ceremony expanded to embrace the news.

Flavia's death, it became clear, was not recent. No. She had slipped down a crevasse on a skiing holiday some years back and now, by chance, the snows had shifted and her remains been recovered and brought home. Hands raised to touch Anne's cheek made her feel like a stand-in corpse – indeed like two corpses since Mummy now was being mourned as well. How had *she* died, someone asked. Illness? Cancer? Ts.

The Marchesa put a stop to this. 'Enough!' she told her guests. 'This poor girl will think she's crossed the Styx. I didn't intend receiving you like this,' she told Anne. 'You're early. I'd supposed . . .'

At the hint, the dark chorus rose and began to disperse. Not all were women. There was a monsignor who invited Anne to drop by his presbytery for a glass of port.

'Just phone first. I remember your mother well. A sweet, bright girl.'

Anne was pleased for Mummy whose fondness for the villa had sometimes struck her as snobbish. Remorsefully, she wondered whether the snobbishness had not been hers. It had seemed degrading that her mother should remember her time here as the time of her life and keep posting greetings cards to people who might consider her a sort of servant.

'But we were on an equal footing,' Mummy had protested. 'That's what *au pair* means. Besides, I liked them.'

For a long time Anne too had liked the sound of them. Their ride-a-cock-horse name had enchanted her childhood: Cavalcanti. Her picture of them was a discontinuous jigsaw. Some bits bathed in a radiant light. Others had got mislaid.

Dislike of patronage had made her hesitate to accept the invitation which came with the Marchesa's rather late letter of condolence. Then, after some months, a more pressing note arrived pleading that the Marchesa Niccolosa was ill and would appreciate a visit. To Anne, who had just sat for her BA (History), and was exhausted by half a year's cramming and mourning, a stay in Tuscany now looked attractive. She obeyed this second summons, and here she was, feeling oddly shaky and emotional.

A man of forty-five or so – in this line-up he was a youth – introduced himself as Flavia's brother, Guido, someone who – this hit Anne unpleasantly – knew private things about her mother. Guido had witnessed Mummy's adultery.

The reliable Catholic girl, brought here to keep frivolous Flavia in line, had herself slipped from the straight and narrow. Worse: she had passed the memory on to Anne as if it were a pet or a plant too precious to be let die. The thing had taken place two years after Anne's parents' marriage. By stealth. The lover, a friend of Guido's who happened to be riding in the Dublin Horse Show, had mounted Mummy in his spare time.

Don't think that way, Anne! She's dead, you know! I know.

Guido was saying he hoped Anne would enjoy her stay and that the place would not seem dull. He would have dined here on her first evening, but had, alas, to drive a flock of aunts back to Florence. He crinkled his eyes at her.

But her mind was on her mother's lover. Cosimo had been a centaur – no, a sort of god. The thought roused resentment. Anne's own dealings with men had suffered from the shadow of this legend. Passion, in

Mummy's book, excused all, but without a high, hot blaze of it sex was tawdry.

'What's the matter?' one young man had demanded to know when Anne had pushed him off her. 'Am I totally repulsive to you?' he'd asked bitterly.

Not totally, no, but on a scale of ten he must rate top marks if she was to feel warrantably carried away – and desire assessed was often desire deflated. Even a strong urge, even one which had begun to soar like a fever patient's temperature could, she had found, sink under scrutiny to seven, six or even five and a half. In self-defence she must find out more about Cosimo. Perhaps meet him? She imagined a mature man with a paunch and was reminded of being taken on the knee of a department-store Santa Claus when she was really too old for this. The old man had smelled of tobacco and cough drops. He was neither strange nor magical – yet magical expectations hung about him and she had yearned to be argued out of her mistrust. Illusion is more fun than the discovery that you are sitting on the knee of someone paid to wear a red dressing gown and a cotton beard. On the other hand, it is exhilarating to find things out and Anne had in the end held it against her mother that she buoyed up a damaged myth. Mummy's reluctance to acknowledge disappointing truths had left Anne leery of fantasy – especially Mummy's. Clearly, if *she* was to justify committing adultery while her young husband was with the UN forces in Africa, Cosimo had *had* to be a god. Equally clearly, Anne's own interests were different. Chained to the rock of her mother's romantic principles, was it not her best hope that the rock turn out to be cardboard?

'Au revoir, *cara*.'

The Marchesa was kissing her friends goodbye and they, their mourning tributes paid, were expanding with delicate relief. Pitching like coracles, they nuzzled around her, aged hips canting now to starboard, now to port.

'*A presto!*'

'*Ciao, bella.*'

When they had gone, she let herself collapse in a chair. She had the grey pallor of the dark-skinned and looked drained.

'Next time *they* come,' she told Anne, 'it will be for my funeral. Oh don't think that bothers me.' She made a soothing gesture. 'I think of myself as a traveller at an airport awaiting an unscheduled flight. That needn't mean you'll have a gloomy stay. We'll liven up my wait. Perhaps now, though, you'd better ask Bruni to take you to your room.

Forgive me if I'm abrupt. One never knows how much time one has in airports.'

As Anne turned to leave, the old lady's eyelids, which looked like small, tight walnut shells, had fastened over her eyes.

Bruni was the man in livery. He threw open the shutters in Anne's room. '*Bella?*' he said of the view.

The word could have taken one a long way at the villa and indeed the view was beautiful. It was a stretch of olive groves descending a mild slope, then gathering in pale, gauzy hills topped with some dark foliage which might be ilex. The air was stained green as it sometimes is in Tuscan paintings and the room was high-ceilinged with a red-tiled floor and a stove with a flue as thick, tall and slightly out of true as the trunk of a young tree.

'Is the Marchesa very ill?' Anne asked.

'Ill!' Bruni agreed. 'Old. Angry. She has a lot to put up with.'

'I hope I won't be a strain.'

'Oh, you'll be good for her. It's the people who didn't come who bothered her today! Her grandson didn't and his mother – that's the Marchese's wife – stayed away as well.' Bruni closed an eye. 'It's bad to gossip, but what I say is no secret. Family business is troublesome business, eh, Signorina?'

'I wouldn't know,' Anne told him. 'I haven't got a family.'

Leaning out, she saw swallows circling below. *There* was a word she remembered. Her reading knowledge of Italian was quite good.

'*Rondini!*' she said proudly to Bruni who leaned beside her to look.

'*Macchè rondini!*' he contradicted. '*Son pipistrelle.*' Not swallows, bats. It was a pinprick to romancing. She laughed and so did Bruni, showing teeth the colour of chopped hazelnuts. 'It's good to have someone young in the house,' he told her. 'We say laughter nourishes. It makes you fat.'

'Why doesn't the grandson visit?'

Bruni lowered his voice. 'Politics.'

'Politics?'

'Sh!' Bruni put a hand to his lips and tilted his head sideways. There was someone at the door.

A tall, gaunt woman wearing a pod of white apron stood in its opening holding a stack of towels. She was perhaps fifty and her eroded face had scarcely a scrap of flesh on it. When she smiled, however, her teeth were as healthy as a young animal's and the flash of them picked up the light in her eyes and showed that she had once been a beauty.

'I'm Ida,' she said. 'Would you like me to help you unpack?'

'*Bene, bene!*' Bruni made a sideways move which could be construed as a semi bow. 'I'll yield the honours to la Ida.' There was a touch of mockery to this which might or might not have been malicious. He left. Ida put the towels on the bed.

'If you need anything ironed,' she offered, 'I can do it right away. You'll want to wear something dressier than what you've got on for dinner. The Marchesa is expecting company.'

Anne, who had had no experience of big-house visiting, wondered how much she would be expected to tip Bruni and Ida and maybe others. What was her status here? Guests tipped, but wasn't she partly on Bruni and Ida's level? Not if Ida was going to do her ironing. She must ask the Marchesa. It felt odd to have someone dancing attendance on her – but then mightn't offering to do her own ironing be taken as a snub?

Ida picked a silk shirt from Anne's open suitcase. 'I'll run the iron over this. It's just the thing for this evening. Why don't you lie down? I'll hang your dresses up meanwhile so they can shake out.'

Anne lay down. This mild bullying was balm to her. It soothed memories of those last horrible months when it was Mummy who was the child – sore, neurotic, frightened – and Anne who had to do the bullying. Scenes from that time still sawed through her nightmares. The torpid half-year since Mummy's death had healed nothing. Anne had spent it cramming for her finals, numbing herself with work and failing to renew friendships dropped during the claustrophobic phase of Mummy's illness. The two had spent this in a cocoon of nervy intimacy, dining on trays, drinking tea laced with whiskey at odd hours and seeing less people than either would have done if they had been less close. The closeness predated the illness. It had begun when Anne was fifteen and her father, a captain in the Irish army, was blown to bits by a bomb he was trying to defuse.

Ida closed the shutters and said something about mosquitoes: '*Zanzare!*'

The word buzzed in Anne's ear as she fell asleep and slid into her dream as an image of dark creatures circling her in an undulating pavane.

A banging shutter awoke her and she stumbled to the window to find that the landscape had changed. Twilight was seeping up the sky. Olive leaves flicked from silver to graphite and a chill breeze snaked around her ankles. For moments she felt the anxiety that comes from losing one's bearings during sleep. Turning back to the room, she saw the skirt belonging to the blouse Ida had taken, and thought that this too should be ironed if she was to wear the outfit at dinner.

Pleased at the pretext for seeking out the reassuring Ida, she pulled on her dressing gown and went into the corridor where she tried to guess the villa's layout from the antiphony of banging shutters which had started up. She was considering going back to see if her room had a bell when a maid carrying an oil lamp came by to check the shutters. As the lamp moved, shadows stooped and flew in the clothy gloom, deforming and dramatizing the urns, nymphs and bric-à-brac with which the corridor was stacked. Anne asked where Ida did her ironing. Not here, said the girl. The generator which provided electricity for this half of the villa had broken down. Ida would be in her own flat on the other side of the *cortile*.

'Over there.' She reopened a shutter and pointed across a wide, well-like, stone-paved space. 'Take this corridor, turn left at the corner and take the stairs down.'

Anne set off and, as it had begun to rain, circled the courtyard so as to stay in the shelter of the overhanging eaves. She passed several bricked-up doors surmounted by sculpted horses' heads and guessed that these must be the stables which in Mummy's day had still been in use. Mummy had talked of riding-treks, dancing parties, picnics and visits from the sons of neighbouring villas. As well as this, the household used to spend two months every summer by the sea where social life had been even livelier. The intention had been to marry Flavia off fast for she was not too bright and thought to be at risk Not *retarded*, Mummy had insisted. No, she was a dear and not moronic or anything – just a bit innocent. Childish. An eye had to be kept on her by someone who could mingle in the young people's activities, someone whom both Flavia and her mother could trust.

'You.' Anne had liked this story which started like a fairy tale.

'Yes,' Mummy agreed, 'me. So I had to have the proper dresses and so forth. If I looked like a chaperone, Flavia wouldn't have trusted me, you see, and neither would the young men. So it was given out that I'd come to talk English to her and learn Italian myself. The nuns recommended me. I'd been head girl in my school in Tipperary and I used to wonder whether it was knowing the song that made the Marchesa choose me. She was like that: half frivolous, half severe.' At this point Mummy, aroused to a limp, rueful gaiety, might begin to sing 'Tipperary'. 'Goodbye Piccadilly! Farewell Leicester Square!' Complexities of nostalgia caught Anne off balance. The fever of the sick room flickered fretfully through these memories. Fear. Pain-killers. Consoling little drinks and consoling plunges into Mummy's past which was not, after all, truly consoling since it had finally led nowhere. While trying to ease things for her dying mother, Anne had absorbed a horror of the unlived life. Mummy's stories about the villa didn't even end unhappily. They didn't end at all. They faded out. Yet the fact that she clung to them and that, like a drowning person's dreams, they were with her at the end gave these tatters of old hope depth and brilliance for Anne. Death had got into the inconclusive sequence of anecdotes and given it the dash which had somehow evaded Mummy.

In a fairy tale, the poor chaperone, wearing dresses run up by the Marchesa's dressmaker, would have carried off one of the lusty young men. That hadn't happened. Until the Cosimo incident in Dublin there had been no flirting at all. That was part of the agreement. The Marchesa didn't want to have to chaperone the chaperone. One hint of gossip about *her*, she'd explained pleasantly, and Mummy could pack her bags.

'Young men are hunters,' she'd said. 'That's their nature. *Cacciatori!* It's up to you to discourage them.'

'Didn't the boys think you strange?' Anne had wondered.

'Oh yes.' Mummy was proud of this. 'They called me "the ice maiden" and "the nun". I told them I had a boy back home.'

It had been a time anyway – pre-pill – when girls flirted with prudence. Risks were high if things went wrong.

Anne, pinned in by a rush of rain, marvelled at the quaint world her mother had glimpsed.

'In those days,' Mummy had told her, 'you could be arrested for kissing on a park bench.'

'A Fascist law, I suppose?'

'Fascism was long gone. Do you think I'm your grandmother?'

Money helped then as always. There was talk of girls going to London to have a hymen implanted and to Switzerland with an inconvenient pregnancy. Mummy revelled in the outrageousness and, when Anne praised recent changes in the law for putting an end to hypocrisy, she couldn't see it at all. 'Pish and tush!' she'd say. She had the Irish preference for breaking rather than changing laws, loved things to simultaneously be and not be and had, her daughter thought, come to see obstacles to happiness as part of the happiness. 'Our sweetest songs are those which tell of saddest thoughts,' she liked to quote, and Anne could have sworn that, for her mother, 'sweet' was a synonym of 'sad'. She adored grand opera, especially *Madam Butter-*

fly. Maybe she identified Cosimo with Pinkerton? Maybe only impossible men appealed to her? Anyway, no fellow Anne had brought home had measured up. 'Well, *he'll* not set the Liffey on fire!' she would comment and when Anne said that was just as well, gave her a look of pity. Knowingly or not, she'd put the dead hand of her past on Anne's present and spoiled it.

As usual, resentment made Anne guilty. Mummy was dead. The disconcerting thing was how little this had changed things. Anne still found herself arguing with a ghost who was by now an extension of herself. The impulse to identify or reject – Would I have behaved differently? Am I like her? – made memory narcissistic. It was like giving your attention to someone who is wearing mirror sun glasses.

The rain now began to come at an angle so that the eaves were no longer a protection. Flattened into the hollow of one of the condemned doorways, she thought she heard movements behind it? A horse? How could it be? Since she was definitely getting wet, she bunched the skirt she was carrying down the front of her dress and made a run for it to Ida's door. She knocked. There was no answer.

'Ida!'

Stepping backwards into the rain, she looked to see if there were any lights in the windows then, as a movement caught her attention, looked back in the direction from whence she had just come. In a window above the bricked-up doorway a young man stood clearly visible in the still vivid dusk. One of his arms was in a sling which had been covered by a yellow silk scarf. Seeing her look at him, he moved out of sight. Just then Ida's door opened and Anne ran gratefully into its shelter.

Ida dried Anne's hair with a hand drier, skilfully curling the edges over a round brush. Next she ironed the blouse and skirt and sewed up a loose seam.

'This takes me back,' she said, 'to when I used to do things like this for the Contessa Flavia. She was helpless herself. A baby.'

'You're a genius,' said Anne appreciatively. 'How come Flavia was a Contessa if her mother's a Marchesa?'

'By marriage. That marriage broke up though and she used to come back here between . . . episodes. She liked us to cosset her. She couldn't survive alone, you see. But she never let herself go. She always looked smart. You could always tell who she was.'

'Who?'

'Of good stock. She always kept up her appearance.'

'You mean that ... underneath ... ?'

'Well, your mother must have told you.' Ida tapped her temple. 'Old stock ...'

'Good stock, you said.'

'Good! Of course it's good! But families are like wine. You get the odd vintage that goes right off: goes weak as coloured water or old scent.'

Ida sighed, finished strengthening the hem of Anne's skirt, knotted her thread and broke it with her teeth. 'There. That'll hold. Store-bought clothes are badly finished. What else could you expect? They pay the workers by the piece and don't pay them enough. I know because my sister-in-law was a seamstress.'

'Tell me about the Marchese's son.'

'Tell you what about him?'

'Why he wasn't here today.'

Ida's head shied upwards and back. 'Who's been gossiping? Bruni?'

'No.' Anne didn't want to make trouble. 'I think it was the Marchesa herself who remarked on it.'

'Old people make mistakes and get stubborn about them.' Ida's own voice was stubborn. 'The Marchesa's grandson is a fine boy. You'd best be getting back. Dinner's at eight. You can have my umbrella.'

Anne thanked her. Standing by the door, she struggled to raise the umbrella while holding her ironed and mended blouse and skirt on a hanger. Ida came to her aid.

'By the way, who lives there?' Anne jerked her chin at the window where she had just seen the young man with an arm in a sling.

'Where? Nobody. That wing was condemned years ago. The roof is dangerous.'

Anne pointed more precisely. 'There,' she said, 'just over that door. I saw someone there just now when I came in. A man. I heard him too.'

'You couldn't have,' Ida told her. 'You must have seen a reflection in the glass. That building is bricked up and the floors are rotten. Maybe you heard rats?' Firmly, she propelled Anne out the door. 'You'd better hurry now,' she said. 'You'll be late for dinner.'

Anne was so careful not to be late that she reached the drawing room before her hostess. There was a guest there already. Count Bonaccorso — Bobo — Pitti introduced himself as a neighbour and friend of the house who was empowered to offer her a drink.

'Gin? Grape juice? Campari?'

He was a bony man in his seventies whose suit hung flat from his shoulders. Vertical lines predominated in his face and achieved an effect of fluting in the folds which flanked his Gothic nose. He had been rearranging some framed photographs on a side table and given prominence to a signed one from the former King of Italy, Umberto.

'Our hostess,' the Count spoke in over-perfect English, lingering on the ends of words, 'may be a trifle late. A heavy day, I gather. Like Niobe, she has been mourning her children. Talking of children, may I ask you a question? Would you have known from my accent that I had an Irish nanny?'

'No,' said Anne.

The Count looked pleased. His family, he explained, had preferred Irish nannies for religious reasons, but he worried about the accent. 'It is charming for an *Irish* person to have an Irish accent,' he hastened to explain, 'but an Italian with an Irish accent would be a bit farcical, don't you think?' He added that he liked the Irish. They were so much less middle-class than the English.

'My nanny taught me three words of Gaelic,' said the Count and gave her what his nanny might have called 'an old-fashioned look'. Unfortunately, the words meant 'kiss my arse': *póg mo hón*. He hoped Anne wasn't annoyed? 'Blame Nanny Doyle.' He shook a steeple of penitent fingers at her, but she saw that the impropriety delighted him.

'I hope you won't mind my repeating them to *you*,' said Anne, 'but, you see, your Gaelic is much too English.' She then repeated *póg mo hón* correctly so many times that she saw him grow a trifle vexed. 'Did she teach you anything else?' she asked conciliatingly.

'Oh yes,' said the Count. 'She taught me and my father before me to wash. People of our class were all taught to wash by nannies from the British Isles. We were washing when nobody else in Italy was,' he said grandly. 'Then in 1944, the Americans came and taught the rest of the population. That's when *they* learned: 1944.' Was there a note of regret? Anne could not be sure. 'However,' the Count concluded with triumph, 'the washing styles differ. They get under the shower. *We* tend to wash piecemeal with basins and bidets. Empire style, wouldn't you guess? Devised perhaps for keeping clean in the bush and on the move?'

Anne agreed with this heroic view of things and the Count, restored and perhaps eager to make up for *póg mo hón*, began to talk of the Irish as dashing hippophiles. Anne was about to use the opening to ask if the Count knew Cosimo when another guest arrived. This was the Marchesa's doctor, a small, tobacco-coloured man in a worn silk suit who shone all over like a much-used coin. He was bald, tanned, bespectacled, smiled a lot and had just been examining the Marchesa.

'She's frail,' he warned. 'More than she thinks. We mustn't annoy her.'

'It's you who annoy her,' said the Count. 'Your politics ...'

'*My* politics ...'

Talk slipped into an Italian obscure with acronyms and became hard to follow as the small doctor worked himself into a passion. Saliva flew and he kept catching gobbets of it as though they were flies, wiping them with his handkerchief and excusing himself. 'Sorry, sorry!' he interjected as he removed one from the Count's lapel. Recognizable words bobbed on a tide incomprehensible to Anne. 'Scandalous!' she heard, then 'cynical' and 'crime'.

'Come, come,' the Count rallied in a wise voice. 'Mustn't get worked up.'

'I *will* say it!' Indignation made the little doctor's voice crack and do odd slides. 'The citizens,' he quavered, 'are castrated and ...'

'*Dottore!*' The Count barked out the word as though training a dog and the little man snapped to, his nervous system responding as clearly his raging mind could not. There was a centrifugal fragility to him. His hair, his skin and even his old silk suit looked ready to bristle and moult. His knee vibrated. His shoe tapped. He stared at the glass in his hand then raised and drank some of its stormy contents.

'You said yourself,' the Count reminded him, 'that the Marchesa mustn't be upset.'

'Too many people,' the doctor's voice was again on the rise, 'are protected from being upset. Censorship ...'

'Truffles!' roared the Count in his parade-ground yell. 'A little bird told me we're to have them for dinner.'

The Marchesa had arrived. 'Bobo!' she exclaimed. '*Dottore!* What a pair of materialists you are! Politics and truffles! Have you met Anne?'

The two men attended her passage to what must be a favourite chair. She wore a dress which had, in motion, something of the sail, the pennant and the flag, yet fell, when she sat, into neat, shipshape lines.

Anne, she told them, had come to keep her company. Wasn't that kind? Yet who was to amuse *her*? Young people liked to dance. Did they know of any dancing partners around here now? No? She turned from prospects of dancing to memories of it. She herself had once waltzed and tangoed like a – a what? 'Help me out, Bobo.' Tilting a softly valanced chin, the old head wobbled flirtatiously.

'Like a swan?' tried the Count.

This was rejected. Swans' feet were broad, she told him. Broad and flat. Hers had been high-arched and nimble. They had skimmed and careened. Her hands, bright with jewellery, made circles in the air. Now they were like roots. Gnarled. Knotted. Reaching for the earth! The humiliations of age were upon her. Even taking a bath was a hazard. Ida had to help and tonight had been in a tiresome mood. 'Something must have upset her. She nearly let me fall!' Niccolosa's bath, gamely described as a sporting event, reduced her hearers to nervous, slightly uncomfortable hilarity. 'Oh my dears!' she confided, 'you can't imagine the slips and slides!' But when she added that getting into one's bath was a rehearsal for getting into a coffin, the three were caught on the wrong foot. 'No need to look so glum!' she scolded. 'I said the same thing to Monsignor to see if he's lost faith in the promises he's been making all these years. He promised me my just deserts and when I saw his face go glum I saw he must have grave doubts that mine will be the deserts of the just!'

By the time Bruni came to announce dinner she had them laughing again.

Next day, though sunny, was still damp. Steam was shot through with rainbows and the villa looked like blurred images of itself in Mummy's album through which Anne had once more searched for a picture of Cosimo. Many of the snaps had been poorly taken and were pocked with flecks of light. Like time itself, these had begun mutilating the faces of Mummy's subjects while they were still smiling into her viewfinder. Anne recognized spectral, chubby images of Guido and Flavia in tennis whites and a few dark, stylish ones of the Marchesa.

Left all morning to her own devices, she mooned through the ground floor of the villa, then found her way to a walled garden where she admired staked raspberry vines and arrangements of eggplant, peppers and baby marrows. Circling back through the orchard – peaches, apricots – she came on a terrace invitingly furnished with reclining seats, iron tables and plump, terracotta nymphs. Bruni arrived at the same moment with the day's papers. The ink, he warned, was liable to come off on her fingers.

'The Marchesa wears gloves to read them.'

Anne sat down, held *La Nazione* by its margins and, rejecting the first page – words like *strage* and *terrorismo* reminded her too much of home, skimmed short notices about the wine lake, the butter mountain, Polish nepotism in the Vatican and a young man who had murdered his landlady. A study had shown Italian military academies to be the most efficient institutions in the peninsula. The postal and transport services could not hope to compete. But then, consoled a journalist, Italian civilian culture had been conceived in a spirit of irony and discontent and could not be expected to bend to military disciplines. Closing her eyes, Anne thought of last night's dinner. Irony and discontent had certainly sparked through that. At one point the Count had called the doctor a crass materialist.

'A good thing he is!' the Marchesa had declared. 'Why else would he try to cure an old carcass like mine? If he believed in heaven the kind thing would be to send me there with a quick overdose.'

'That,' said the Count who was clearly easy to shock, 'is forbidden by the Church.'

'Well, to be sure,' said the Marchesa. 'If it were not, the faithful would die like lemmings and where would the Church be then?'

This reminded her of more recent pitfalls. Last time Monsignor had taken a holiday, a missionary fresh from the tropics had preached a sermon exhorting the parish to create their heaven here and now in the guise of an improved social system. The Marchesa had written to the bishop. Such fools' bargains might suit the Third World but did not, she assured him, do here. Speaking as one who would soon be on her way there, she wished to register a protest against the Church's bartering God's Kingdom for a few doubtful improvements to this Vale of Tears. Did they want to turn heaven into an upstart republic subject to tribal strife and liable to alienate one's assets?

'I mind about all this,' she told Anne, 'because I'm counting on meeting my ancestors there. Ida's been reading me their memoirs so that I'll know who they are. It's only polite: *They* can't be expected to know about *me*.' Her smile could have been whimsical or pious.

Anne got a sense of these old friends as being indifferent to what was actually said. They plucked at old themes as if weaving a long web of allusion and memory whose design was obscure to her and in whose making she could not join. The Marchesa's monologues were probably variations on earlier ones made here, evening after evening, while the old Count punctuated them with hisses and whistles of disagreement or approval. There was a lazy ceremony to the way they talked, a lack of immediacy, even a droning hum reminiscent of set responses. Dublin, another backwater, polished its effects in just this way, tolerating repetition in the interests of punctilio and form. It was all both novel and familiar and the web of chat was beguiling, like the spectacle of a game whose rules it would not be hard to learn and in which she could look forward to joining before long.

The doctor, who had been drinking silently, now weighed in with a lament to the effect that idealism was a thing of the past. 'I was a partisan,' he mourned. 'I was full of belief. I believed in honesty and purity. I believed in what our songs said.'

'Well, my dear chap,' said the Count, 'at my nanny's knee I learned not to ask for the moon. Nanny Doyle,' he turned to Anne. 'Irish. She taught me some words in Gaelic . . .'

'Yes, so you said!'

'*Up in the mountains*,' sang the doctor, '*under the flowers,/Lie the best and the bravest of their men and ours.* The best are dead. Dead or old. The decent young no longer care for politics.'

'Happily!' said the Count.

'Unhappily!' said the doctor. 'Though there are shining exceptions.'

'We shan't discuss them,' said the Marchesa and nodded to a footman who brought in the pudding.

It was served in an amber-coloured glass bowl. Niccolosa ladled some on to a small plate then, with a smart jab of the spoon, broke the bowl and spooned some of the fragments on to the portion of pudding. The mixture was handed to Anne.

The Count looked at her eagerly. 'You're surprised, aren't you?'

'Yes.'

'Hahahaha!' Nanny Doyle would surely have disapproved of her one-time charge's rowdy laugh. 'It's caramel!' he managed to explain. 'Ha!' he snorted. 'Edible caramel.'

'Quiet, Bobo. Take no notice,' Niccolosa told Anne. 'Take no notice of either of them. Company excites them. They're country mice.'

'Once . . .' began the Count.

'Oh, *once*,' said Niccolosa, 'we were all worldly, but the world, *cari miei*, is backing away from us.'

'I shan't regret it.' The doctor looked sadly at his wine glass.

'Making you think that,' said Niccolosa, 'is one of the world's kinder tricks.'

Anne went back to reading her paper. SCANDALO A ROMA exploded a headline. A cabinet minister's son had fled the country a few hours before the police came to arrest him for belonging to a terrorist group. WHO TIPPED HIM OFF? asked another headline. Two of his confederates had been killed in a police shoot-out described as 'unnecessary and irresponsible'. A third confederate had escaped. DID THEY KNOW TOO MUCH? Suspicion oozed from page to page. Had the minister saved his own son and arranged to have his co-conspirators killed in order to silence testimony about this? Or about worse? Had the boy had access to government secrets? To NATO secrets? Was the CIA involved? Speculation was dizzy. There were photographs of the suspect, the missing and the dead. VATICAN CONNECTIONS? MAFIA CONNECTIONS? Might the masons be involved? By now, as Bruni had warned it might, ink had smeared not only Anne's fingers but her skirt. With the mild curiosity of the safe, she glanced at the faces of the young men who had got themselves on to police files and saw that the fugitive terrorist had an elusively familiar look. He was thought to have been wounded in the shoot-out and was probably lying low in some terrorist haven.

It was almost lunchtime so she bundled up the papers and went to wash her hands.

Passing the library, she heard Ida read aloud in bored tones. 'In the name of God, his mother and all the saints of Paradise,' read Ida, 'I shall now relate ...' She was beginning the memoirs of yet another of the Marchesa's ancestors. Earlier this morning Anne had offered to take a turn reading, but her accent had not proven sufficiently good. Having heard half an hour of a fourteenth-century cloth-merchant's diary, she was just as glad. It was less a diary really than a ledger: so many wives, dowries, surviving children, miscarriages, losses, deaths. All were reducible to figures and totted up 'for the benefit of those who shall come after me'. If the Marchesa spent time with the writer of this, she was going to have a dull time in heaven.

'Reading about one's forbears can be chastening,' she had remarked to Anne. 'This man, as Ida will tell you, is glamour itself compared to some we read about on my mother's side. Very small folk. One was a fellow who made his living dredging sand from the Arno in the thirteenth century, and *his* grandson was a purse-maker whose shop on the Ponte Vecchio was destroyed by floods. Very ordinary. But tough. Ours is tough stock. Rotten branches may fall, bastard lines take over, but the stock survives. We're like olive trees. Did you know that olive trees can live up to two thousand years? Well, they can.'

Anne and two quick-eyed, fidgeting children belonging to the *fattore* had been roped in to play Monopoly with the Marchesa. The game was based on Florence, and the ceramic board had been designed by

Flavia at a time when she had found an alibi in pottery for some lagging on the marriage market.

'That was just after your mother left,' said Niccolosa. 'An idle girl, as the proverbs say, is at risk, so when Flavia was suddenly without a chaperone we had to invent interests for her.'

Anne hadn't known that Mummy had left suddenly. Something about the way this was said made her hesitate to ask the question the old lady was expecting. When it didn't come, Niccolosa created further openings for it, needled, waited and cast sidelong glances at Anne. She seemed to be angling – but for what? Deviousness – Anne had seen this in Mummy – might well be second nature to the dying. Truth frightens them but must be coped with, so they develop strategies for enticing it, plan measures to be taken then, with deft speed, dodge direct acknowledgement. But what was Niccolosa dodging now? Perhaps the Marchesa – sometimes Anne thought of her by her title, sometimes by her first name as though they were toing and froing between intimacy and hauteur – perhaps the sick woman was simply incapable of facing anything at all head on? Any dodging could be practice for the final skirmish.

Anne had the impression – it was clear that the children did too – that Niccolosa had cheated just now at the Monopoly game. They were playing out of doors and the sun caused the old lady to lower the hoods of her eyelids so that the eyes beneath gleamed with the sliced brightness of deep wells.

'You're not playing sensibly,' Niccolosa scolded one of the children. 'You must keep some cash. If you don't, how will you pay me rent if you land on one of my streets?' Her great, spherical bust swung to and fro with the ease of one of those toys which cannot tilt over because they're weighted at the base. 'You'd have to mortgage your houses,' she warned the child. 'You'd have to give them back to Miss Ryan at a loss.'

Anne was bank because Niccolosa's stiff, old fingers had trouble sorting the flimsy, imitation banknotes.

'In their day,' Niccolosa told the children, 'the English were great bankers. So, of course, were the Florentines. An English king cheated them very badly though. King Edward III never paid his debts to the Bardi and Peruzzi who were both connections of my own family. Eight hundred thousand florins he welshed on: a tremendous sum! Not,' she added as an afterthought, 'that Miss Ryan is exactly English.'

The children stared at Anne and were perhaps wondering whether this made her less than exactly honest and in debt to the Marchesa.

'Ha! I've landed on the via dei Bardi and shall buy it if you please, Anne.' Niccolosa collected the deeds as though performing an act of piety and conquest. It was, Anne saw, in order to land her counter on this favoured street that she had manipulated the dice. The game was a mnemonic, her purpose not to win but to be stirred.

'There!' she had tidied her assets into piles and was perceptibly taking possession not only, it struck Anne, of the Monopoly board, but of Anne herself: a vacant lot, she must feel. Emotionally vacant. Available. Was this fancy? No. Anne felt sure that what she sensed was the old lady's sly, predatory approach.

'Flavia,' said Niccolosa, as though mind-reading, 'was the wrong sort of daughter for me. It's hypocrisy to say one shouldn't speak ill of the dead. It's surely better to speak the truth about them than to forget them. We weren't suited to each other at all. Your turn.' She handed Anne the dice.

Jeremy Reed

Six Poems

JEREMY REED was born in the fifties in Jersey in the Channel Islands. Amongst his previous publications are *Bleecker Street* from Carcanet Press, and amongst his forthcoming *By the Fisheries* from Jonathan Cape, and a novel *The Lipstick Boys*. In 1982 he was a recipient of a major Eric Gregory Award, and also a prizewinner in the National Poetry Competition.

The Storm

A wasp's vibration in a gorse-flower,
that orange flame belling the wings' motion,
was how it seemed miles distant, the tremor

of a needlehead dropped from a great height
into the uncorked bottleneck we cooled
in a sea-pool. All afternoon the light

blazed iridescently ultramarine
on a sea surface fixed like an eye-glass
into the peacock of the horizon;

the hours afloat, and a torpid sea-bell,
leisurely tinkling; and you with a pen
and red ink, fashioned a memorial

to the dead seagull found upon the cliff
in our descent. A gruff buzz of black flies
sounded like a kitten's purr on the path

as they stippled that carrion. And down
below, the calm was eerie, and the lull
seemed like the sky and sea stood still, one calm

reflection, lacquered over with gold flecks
in lapis lazuli. We trod water,
or lay immobilely upon our backs

cushioned by the salt bay; and then it grew
this hairline of cobalt, to a fissure
of massing cloud, an ink-dot in the blue

expanding to a welled concentration
of angry mauves, and marbled quartz, and red,
and we could hear the thunder's vibration

stalk like a big cat growing voluble
behind the incandescence of its cage.
Then rain, each drop shiningly audible,

clopping into the sea, and shimmering
with a dragonfly's bright translucency,
each globule expanding to a white ring.

We took refuge before the downpour steamed
cleansingly through crevice and flaw, and smoked
skywards. You drew the lightning flares as red

unskewered spiral hairpins jumpingly
illuminating a cobalt skydrop,
while I saw the future, a butterfly

escaping its chrysalis, and on stone,
resting a while, before the longer flight,
sure like the migrant swallow of its home.

To Him Away

Today, our son, my Lord, was much estranged,
     being most lately come
from Gheel, where certain wandering madmen
impressed his youth with black omens,
     so that he walks with tonsured head,
or broods distractedly for hours
     upon the progress of the sun.
I fear he is no longer ours

in sense, and pleasure's to him alien.
     He keeps himself above
a young man's passion to despoil or love,
and is a hawk become a dove.
     I fear the promised union
with Sherbourne's fairest is amiss,
     and increase of estate removes
itself. My Lord I do distress

you, that I know, you being at the wars,
     and rain making a churn
of every country road. Doubtless we turn
to grief most when there's no return
     by messenger or brumous prayer
I despatch in our cold chapel,
     asking of Christ to move our son
into the light, who strangely fell

into this restless torpor. James, my Lord,
     came speaking with half your
tongue, and half his, as becomes a brother,
and thought to let blood would confer
     upon his grandson quietude.
The need is pressing, for he speaks,
     and this alone gives him pleasure,
of making gold in a retreat,

as lately certain charlatans perform.
      I ask you to renege
all lands promised to him when come of age,
rather, I risk, my Lord, your rage,
      by writing I forbid. Your scorn
at first, must not cloud your reason.
      Think, landless, nothing would assuage
your broken pride before the Queen.

The evening bell, and I must late give seal
      to this troublesome news.
I beg you ponder how your son eschews
all reason, before you review
      with what physic we may expel
the mad forebodings of his brain.
      My Lord, as we, pray for our souls.
I send you good tidings: your Jane.

Conger

A conger's world is tubular, it means
seeing things thinly through a gun-barrel
from the point of view of the bullet-head
that's primed to fire, the fist-sized, clam-tight jaws

more deadly in their lock than a bulldog's.
They'll shave a finger off with precision,
clean as a horse bite, or close round a hand
and leave it as taut gristle strung on bone.

The colour of beached wrack, or an old tom
that's greying, these inhabit wrecks, or lairs
from which their protruding head is streamlined
like a grounded jet's. Fastened to a spar

they'll fight on a short fuse, and savagely
bite free of suction pads working to grip
the powerful torsion of the body's girth.
In biting, their mouth opens from a slit

to an alsatian's wide full-toothed gullet.
Conger stay low, anchored to the sea-bed,
solitary killers holed up in their dens,
they mostly go unchallenged, like this head

which would swallow a sewer-rat or cat
washed out to sea; ingorge it, and lie low
until nightfall, and then seek out new prey,
killing with a psychopath's will to slow

the moment to all time. Dragged to the air,
a conger barks, and if not killed outright
will live a day, and still retaliate.
This black boothead dazzled by a boat-light,

come loose of the hook, might jump at a throat,
and drag a man down, who stands shrinking back,
petrified at this one to one combat;
a jerky lighthouse twitching through the black.

Dogfish

A sensibility of teeth; down there,
plumb-bottom, where the light is diffused smoke,
and what moves, dares that green opacity,
is where one finds you, your round toe-capped snout

raised at the height of a rat-trap from sand
shelving to stone where the conger's snake-head
stokes in its rock lair, and decapitates
an unsuspecting wrasse. What are the dead

to the sea's predators – the millions
of carrion subsumed daily, eaten
before they're dead, or falling to the depths,
scavenged? Nothing has time to go rotten

or stiffen out. The sea would eat the sea
if it had jaws, not the mere force of weight.
And this one, lacking a shark's toothed bonnet,
is still ferocious, and its gut a freight

of green crabs, wrasse, and the sand-stippled plaice.
Spotted, its desert-tank markings disguise
its basking, dredging the sea-floor at night
for flesh split open, fig-ripe, mauve. Its eyes

are set at a pig's angle to its snout,
a lesser shark, it is lobotomized
of the insatiable rip-cord to kill.
The one I hooked had never realized

that space is everywhere there isn't sea,
lashing out on the boat-boards, blinded by
a hurricane lamp, spotted like a log
coming to life, agonized with surprise

at a split-second world that's alien.
For man the reverse process would punch out
his oxygen, and cramped into the cold,
he too might cry, and pressure freeze his shout.

Christopher Smart in Madness

They spare me Bedlam for St Luke's Shoreditch,
who am appointed heir to King David,
and fester here where rabid
cries accompany Battie's enquiry
as to madness, whence comes this divine itch
to see into the limits of the sky?
I trundle God's gold ball in Satan's ditch.

They bait me like a bear. My creditors
are importuning demons who'd usurp
my episcopal claims. They hurt
my fevered head, and festinate the ague,
so that I shrink back in my noisome lair,
and crouch there, distracted, unwitting, vague.
The fire of ADORATION burns my hair.

My wife's a Moabite, a Newbery
for whom I squandered my pen in burlesque
before the angelic lyre struck
my holiness to David. Now I pray
that all hurt things are of one ministry.
Listen, the redbreast sings in February,
appointed angel to our misery.

And I am delivered from London's news,
its pettifogging brawls. Johnson alone
gives meat to a dead skeleton
of words; and came by. How his linen stank,
like mine. His strength prevents him breaking through
to the other side of reason. I drank,
before a red cloud opened in the blue,

and I prayed vociferously to God,
and bound myself to the purgative wheel
which burnt the lining of my soul.
Jubilate Agno, they'd confiscate,
except my mind's like a worm in a clod,
which cut in half can still compose, secrete,
and render consecration to David.

Cuckolded, cheated of inheritance,
I shiver here, and hear the sudden bell
of Staindrop Church. Lilac umbels
chequered the grass, the wild polyanthus,
I picked for one Anne Hope, and then in trance,
saw our heavenly marriage through stained glass.
God's voice was further then. I had distance.

And now a pauper go. My alms are words
of prophecy. God lit my candlestick's
orange and immutable wick,
but still they never see. Harping-irons
prod us to tasks, who cower here in dread,
and see rats catch the bread for which we pine,
and hungry, live upon raw gin instead.

Let Peter rejoice with the white moon fish
that's radiant in the dark, and let attend
Jesus on us, unsound of mind,
who cured Legion. My brethren here despair
of light, and must in other madhouses
repine for day; and go without repair.
I pray so loudly that the others curse.

The prison dampness comes to coat my skin
who venture in God's fire, and see the stone
on the right hand side of his throne
withheld from man. And gold within the dark,
I see the mine of Hell where the napkin
of the escaped Jesus still redly marks
the stone, and brooding on it I see Cain.

Outside it rains. I hear a horse collapse,
and men beat it ferociously with sticks.
It died. I pray God for redress
of all animal injuries. Tonight
I wept, and thought to incur a relapse,
and in his knowledge God brightened his light.
Tonight Christ's lantern swings inside this house.

Buoys

Punch drunk are worked over,
beleaguered by each sea's
top-spin of swell, lathered
and pitched to queasily

restabilize, they are ochre
pumpkin-heads pocked with rust shale
in a whorl of white water,
grouting like snouts in a pail

in the momentary backwash
of Atlantic welter.
To seagulls they're atolls,
to the tern flying saucers,

and obesely unsinkable,
they are a boxer's nightmare
of a face repeatedly hit
that won't blackout, but stays there.

They are bulk opposing a sea
that never stops running, markers
of dangerous shoals, their bells
warning off intruders

gruffly as farm-dogs. Herded
out across nautical charts,
they are inshore satellites,
playing their rumbustious parts

for all sea-craft. Vigilant bulls
confined to marking time,
they too in their anchorage
tug at a nose-chain,

and snore hoarsely in storm,
the sea waterbug-green,
beneath a sky black
as a cormorant's sheen.

Two I see wintering
at grass in a shipping yard,
veterans of long wars,
their grizzled tonsures hard

with resilience, awaiting
new paint, their cyclopean
eyeballs gone rusty from staring
unlidded at the ocean.

Keith Roberts

The Silence of
the Land
In homage to Vercors

KEITH ROBERTS was born in Kettering, Northamptonshire, and works as a graphic designer and copywriter. Of his numerous books the best known is undoubtedly *Pavane*, an alternate timestream novel concerned with the success of the Spanish Armada. This and several other titles are shortly to be reissued.

*T*he ghosts were more than usually visible today. The closer sky-line, the long slope behind the trenches, shimmered with them; they passed on and down, bowed by fatigue, by knowledge heavier than the weight of their great packs. Between them the limbered guns showed clear, like pale holes knocked in the sky; the horses too were silhouettes, the colour of a range of distant hills. Around and above them burst a desultory barrage. The flashes, equally silent, yet impinged; each one a gust of quiet, muting the rustling of trees. Some-where beyond, the towers of Ypres town were lost in bright sun-haze; beyond again, flat fields of Flanders stretched out to the sea. This though was an inland place; enclosed, remote.

Kaeti wobbled her way up the long, straight lane, steered for the wicket gate beside the little caff. As ever, her front tyre bumped the wood aside. The tyre was brown and smooth, of funny thirties rubber; from the rear bracket of the bicycle hung the rotted remnants of a dress guard. Its chrome parts too were rusted, to a bright squirrel red.

She pushed the bike beneath a small lean-to, walked to the beaten path that led to the first of the trenches. She stood a moment staring with her wide-set, green-brown eyes; then turned back to unlock the rear door of the place. She padded through the long, low room beyond, where the *minnenwerfers* squatted like bulky idols. She crossed the bar with its floor of dull lino tiles, unbolted the front door and stood it slightly ajar. She stared again, across the rutted gravel where the coaches parked. Below a little shoulder of rising ground, a plot of land was fenced with wire and posts. A wooden shack was partly screened by bushes; beside it a sandpit was covered by a rough timber hatch. A board was nailed up crookedly; fat white letters proclaimed the place as PRIVAT. Beside her the howitzer squatted grimly on its wheels, its trail sunk deep in tilth. Its muzzle, sullenly withdrawn, barely projected from the massive shield; the breech, as thick through as her body, was stained with fine brown mould. Above, the tree leaves rustled, rich with the first hint of autumn; to the right the track ran curving by the wood, rose again to the Canadian Memorial, lost among further trees.

A wasp buzzed in the little room, trapped behind grubby nets. Kaeti turned back, walked behind the counter. Beside it, framed by brass and copper, stood a bulky, head-high clock. The columns that supported it were great shell cases; its dial was haloed by glittering rings of bullets. She took a cloth up from beneath the counter, then once more paused. It was as if for a moment she contemplated polishing the thing, burnishing that which already gleamed; then she turned away. For all its obtrusiveness, the trophy seemed possessed of a curious unreality; it seemed her hand might pass clear through the metal. She laid the cloth back down, and filled a kettle instead.

The engine of the car was audible for a minute or more before the vehicle appeared. It nosed into the little clearing with a certain caution, as if its driver was still unsure of the rules of this new and dusty road. Kaeti stared. It was a curious machine, high-sided and with thin, spoked wheels; almost like the old vans in the museum stereoscopes. It turned, reversed and disposed itself neatly beside the farther trees. A door opened, clicked; there was the little scrunch of footsteps. The nearer door opened in turn, a passenger emerged with care. The driver joined him; and both men stood awhile, regarding the mighty gun. They moved forward then, to the entrance of the caff. Kaeti plugged the kettle in, and turned.

The driver was well built, and tall. He wore the remnants of what could easily have been a military blouse; his trews, of some heavy, workaday cloth, were of the same nondescript hue while his boots, at which he suddenly glanced with a faint air of embarrassment, were heavily spattered with a whitish mud. His chestnut-brown hair stuck up at cheerfully uncombable angles; his strong-boned face was gaunt, his eyes a piercing blue. His companion was very old indeed; once tall perhaps but stooping now and frail, his hair and neat moustache snow-white. He was dressed in well-worn tweeds, a spotted kerchief peeping from his breast pocket; and despite the warmness of the day he wore a short topcoat. The hand he rested lightly on the nearest table top was maimed, two fingers partly lost from some old wound.

The younger of the two continued for a moment to stare down. When he raised his head it was with an air of slight surprise; as if his vision had been narrowed, he had only slowly become aware of the clock, the girl, the little tables set around, the lino-chequered floor. He smiled, and frowned; but silence must be broken. '*Bon après-midi,*

Mam'selle,' he said uncertainly. *'Deux filtres, s'il vous plaît; un blanc, un noir . . .'*

'It is all right,' said Kaeti quickly. 'I do speak English.'

It seemed the other visibly relaxed; but the uncertainty did not wholly leave him. 'Thank you,' he said. 'Two coffees, please; one white, one black.' His voice, well modulated, was soft.

Kaeti said, *'Merci, M'sieu'.'* She turned away, set out the squat, thick cups, filled them with boiling water. Behind her she heard a scraping, the faint creak of a chair.

'It is quiet here today,' said the younger man. 'Usually I expect there are many more folk. Charabanc parties and such. I suppose it is coming to the end of the season.'

Kaeti glanced up, and busied herself again.

'We have come a considerable way,' said the other. 'From Wevelghem. At least it seemed a considerable way to me. I am still not accustomed to driving on the right side of the road.' He considered. 'In English, that is a joke,' he said. 'Perhaps in French as well.'

Kaeti emptied the cups, and dried them. She placed the plastic filters over them, refilled with hot water. She set them on a tray, added a sachet of brown sugar and a tiny carton of cream. She served the visitors; the younger glanced at the tariff board and paid her, carefully though still it seemed with puzzlement, his sixty francs. 'Thank you,' he said again.

He glanced around him. 'This is a big land,' he said inconsequentially. 'Such a very big land.' He raised the lid of one of the little filters, set it back. 'Yesterday,' he said, 'we came through Armentières. There were green trees. It was all somehow so different. The rooflines of the buildings were different too; we could never have mistaken it for England. But of course I expected that. One grows accustomed to it.' He became reflective, seemed for a while to lose himself in thought. 'Last night,' he said finally, 'we were in Ypres. We found a *pension* that sold us Dover soles. There was wine vinegar on the table.' He smiled. 'In England one does not often see wine vinegar.'

Kaeti set glasses in the little dural sink, and turned on the tap. The driver stared a moment longer, then turned to his companion. They conferred together, their voices barely disturbing the quiet; finally the old man levered himself to his feet. His companion would have risen to assist him; but the other raised a hand. The gesture was a gentle one; but there was in it an authority, a calm quality of strength that was not, it seemed, to be denied. The younger man sat back. 'My friend will visit the museum,' he said, perhaps unnecessarily. 'Then he will go to the trenches, just for a little while. He will wish to be alone; he was here once before.'

Kaeti rinsed the glasses one by one, and stood them on the draining board. She began to dry them, polishing absently with a cloth. Her eyes were on the open door.

The other followed the direction of her glance. Outside, the gun still loomed. He smiled again. 'The hydraulics have failed,' he said. 'The barrel is in the full recoil position. Perhaps one day it can be restored.' He sipped at his coffee. 'The wheels, I think, do not belong to it,' he said. 'Such thin little things would never have borne its shock.'

He turned back, set the cup down. He felt in his pockets, produced a much battered briar pipe. He prodded at it, peered into the bowl, looked disturbed again. He ran fingers through his hair, considered. Finally he said, 'Do you mind me talking to you a little?'

Kaeti put away the last of the glasses. She glanced back to him, lips pursed, and reached to empty the sink. The water gurgled round the little plunger, audible in the quiet afternoon.

The other glanced along the lane. 'Nobody else will come,' he said. 'Not for a little while.' He spoke it with a certain calm conviction, yet still with a trace of puzzlement. He turned back. 'This may be a slightly odd remark,' he said, 'but I sense a critical experience. I don't pretend to understand it, not as yet; perhaps I never will. But at least I recognize it. A moment of stasis; what we would call a node.' He lit the pipe, puffed a little cloud of aromatic smoke. He nodded toward the rear of the place, the museum room and the trenches. 'He was my tutor,' he said. 'A long while ago. Nearly half a lifetime.' He puffed again. 'He expected great things of me,' he said. 'But I fell away. Perhaps we all fall away. To be with him now, after so very long; I sense a certain ... privilege.'

Kaeti watched him thoughtfully. He seemed too young ever to have been taught by such a very old man; though when he turned, the brightness altered on his cheek, there was a haggard quality that made him ageless.

He rested his hands in his lap. 'The work I was doing,' he said. 'It no longer met his standards. I decided it for myself.' He shook his head. 'It is a bad thing to fall from grace,' he said. 'One takes paper and a pen; and one is alone. Always alone. One answers to oneself; so there can be no forgiving. I wonder if that is not the hardest part of all.' He brooded. 'Perhaps it is the place,' he said. 'This place. I find it somehow ... surprising. I did not expect to find a café here.' He watched the squares of sunlight on the floor. Finally he looked up. 'I don't think I was here at all just then,' he said. 'Not for that little while. There was . . . another room, also with the sunlight streaming in. Through big tall windows. There were pine trees, off in the distance over roofs; and he was teaching me.' He sucked at the pipe. 'The sentences of English were the girders of a bridge,' he said. 'The commas and full stops, they were its rivets. Where the bridge went to; that was another matter. He said that that was for each of us to decide.' He tapped the pipe out. 'The War was a man's affair,' he said. 'His War. I think perhaps I fell away in that respect as well.'

Kaeti folded the tea towel neatly, and laid it on its shelf. Others were tossed into a little heap; she began to sort them, slipping the grubbiest into a plastic bag.

'We always sat alphabetically,' said the other. 'I think if I tried I could still reel off the first two rows. My place was in the right-hand corner, at the back. Easy to doze; but never when he was there. It came so easily to me; I always wondered why the others sat and sucked their pens.' He looked reflective. 'The swots would shoot their hands up to him; palm forward, like a sort of odd salute. And the jockeying for favour; "*Sir, Sir, Sir* . . ." Lordy, they'd hiss like geese. But he was never impressed. I couldn't ever be bothered; I'd get bored, start to read on ahead.'

Some shadow crossed his face; the beginning of a frown. 'He told me once,' he said, 'the best jobs went to the clever and lazy. In that way too, he had some hope of me. But at the end he couldn't hold me. Not even him. The world was too much with me; girls were a gingham menace.' He examined the pipe as if it were the most curious of objects, seen for the very first time. 'Straw hats in the sun,' he said. 'All those well-scrubbed legs and arms. And eyes, always the almond eyes. So many mistakes to make.' He turned back briefly to glance at the great gun. 'I thought there would be answers,' he said. 'We all thought there would be answers. Something final, total. Beyond dispute. But there were only more questions. So very many questions.'

Kaeti considered. Then she collected his cup and saucer, stacked them in the sink. She prepared a fresh filter, steeped it and took it to him. He said solemnly, 'Thank you.'

He sat back. 'Memory is stasis,' he said slowly. 'The node, the frozen moment. We don't remember movement, we don't remember joy. The sunlight is on the desks; so until the image fades, I'm still sixteen. Perhaps at least that's something learned.' He lifted the filter carefully from the cup. 'I was looking for something,' he said. 'I suppose we all were, in our separate ways. Maybe I still am; I can't remember.'

He produced a leather tobacco pouch, began to refill the pipe. 'In one sense,' he said, 'there's nothing here at all. Just farmhouses, the little lines of trees. In another, there is more than could be dreamed.' He tamped the pipe. 'I thought there would be great truths to be found,' he said. 'Great revelations. Egocentricity of course; a name for the human condition. There's only one revelation; that Fact is Fact. It's the hardest lesson of all.' He paused. 'Hill Sixty is a spoil tip,' he said. 'Just a spoil tip. Forty feet of muck. A game of King of the Castle; only the rules had changed.' He shook his head. 'I had a room in England once,' he said. 'A gas meter in the corner, and the books stacked up all round. All that was left of another sort of dream; but I wouldn't have missed the dreaming. Not for all the world.' He turned the coffee cup curiously, studying the small, neat crest. '*Rombouts*,' he said. 'It is certainly very fine.' He glanced up. 'Perhaps I shall be in England again tomorrow,' he said. 'I do not think good coffee is sold there any more.'

Kaeti turned away. The clock ticked sonorously; and the wasp had begun to buzz again. Momentarily, the sounds of both machine and insect faded.

'Like great sails flapping,' said the visitor reflectively. 'How exact. How very *exact*.' He glanced toward the trenches. 'How he would love a phrase like that,' he said. 'How he loved phrases. He'd roll them round his tongue, and savour them. Like wine. Or perhaps I judge too lightly. After all, I was still a child.' It seemed he communed with himself, held some inner debate; for finally he nodded. 'Precision was his concern,' he said. 'Above all that. Precision is the only vital thing; at least I learned so much.' He frowned. 'Precision is understanding,' he said finally. 'And understanding is defence. We must defend ourselves, against a Fact like this. Against all Facts.'

He lit the pipe carefully, tamping again with his forefinger; as carefully extinguished the match, placed it in the scratched tin tray in front of him. 'Always the silence,' he said. 'Even when the little radios were playing, even when there were other folk about. I thought at first it was things that couldn't speak; then I thought it was things that spoke too loud.' He turned the pipe in his hands, and rubbed the bowl. 'We went to Spanbroekmolen,' he said. 'The lilies grow well there, out from the edge of the lake. If you walk the fields round about, there's still the Iron Harvest.' He considered again. 'Last night we were in Ypres,' he said. 'There were Indian names on the Menin Gate. Havildars and jemadars. For a time, I thought I understood. The Gotama knew the same centrality; I thought I was a step along the road.

But now I'm no longer sure.' He nodded toward the windows. 'The treestumps in the wood,' he said. 'Those old, old stumps. They're rotten, all shored up; and the saplings springing to spite them, all round about.' He shook his head. 'They're not real, you know. Not any more. The gun's not real. You could push it aside one-handed.'

Kaeti looked thoughtful. Then she picked a dishcloth up, began methodically wiping down the tables. The wasp finally found its way into the open air; the buzz increased, and faded. She finished, went back to the bar, washed her hands and dried them, wiped them on her jeans. His eyes followed her; but distantly. 'Ah yes,' he said, 'the cloth *de Nîmes*. And your woollen is old and patched; exactly right.'

She glanced up momentarily, under her brows.

'Such a hard thing to express,' he said. 'But the sparkling wines finally sicken one. I should know; I tried enough of them, in my way. He tried so hard to teach me; but I couldn't learn. Words were his *vin du pays*. Now it's too late of course; but that's unimportant too.' He smiled. 'Another of his tenets. Kindness is common coinage. Taste must diffuse from above.'

He sipped his coffee. 'The Gate,' he said. 'Those sixty thousand names. I think after all the poet got it wrong. Age, finally, is not the thing to fear. They were saved from error, from growing even smaller than they had been at their beginnings. Perhaps that's another thing learned. Death is always a new mistake; it's the ones who are left who fall into the bad old ways. The little snakes start hissing then, always at dead of night.'

Kaeti glanced sidelong. Beyond the café, in the rotting zigzags of the trenches, a tiny shape was visible; the old man's head and shoulders, above a grassy parapet. He sat hunched forward, still; lost as if in intense thought.

'Those were the German lines I think,' said the visitor. 'Lordy though, how they'd crawled forward; so close up under the wood. It wasn't a Sanctuary by then; not any more.' He drew on the pipe. It had gone out; he relit it, with equal care. 'I had a dream last night,' he said. 'In Wevelghem. There was a café, just across the road from where we stayed. The door was banging, there were blasts of music. It woke me several times; eventually I saw a rather fine young man. First he took his skin off, then his inside parts; then he took his bones to pieces, and packed them in a box. I don't quite know how he managed that; it was rather odd.' He paused. 'Then I saw you,' he said. 'You were looking down through clouds. Just like the Nash Madonna. Or maybe they were gunsmoke; it was hard to tell. You smiled, and brushed them away; so I knew you were the only real thing there.' He smiled himself. 'You couldn't call it prescience,' he said. 'It was just that I'd seen you so many times before. We all had.' He toyed with the cup; rotated the handle till it faced the other way, and turned it back. 'Tomorrow, we shall go to Tyne Cot,' he said. 'It won't be real. I've seen reality.'

Kaeti glanced at the clock.

'Ah, the contraction of time,' said the other. 'I have heard of such things. Even experienced them. You will wish to be closing soon; but we shan't hold you up.' He rubbed his lip. 'There was a time,' he said, 'when I would not have spoken. For fear of hurting you. Making you old. But I know now that can never happen. The gun will rust; but the gun is only steel.' He slipped the pipe into his pocket. 'Once,' he said, 'I had a great desire. To follow you, and Know. And when the hairs of your head were numbered, and the dust grains on your shoes ...' He laughed. 'I made a great machine,' he said. 'All knobs and big brass dials. And crosshairs, calibrations; it was very clever. I'd turn the controls, and I could follow you; I'd see you eat an apple, watch you brush your teeth. Morning to night, till the figure finally closed, the equation solved itself.' He shook his head. 'It was a phase though; just another phase. So many false directions. The machine was in my mind; I don't need it any more.' He rose. 'It's time,' he said. 'I shall go and fetch my friend.'

She followed, at a little distance. By the first of the trenches, protruding from the path, was the blackened rim of a great shell. He stepped past it delicately, bent over the old man. She saw the other nod and rise, content at last that his arm should be supported. She held the gate; and the pair stepped through and on beyond the gun, grown shadowy now with the lessening of light. The car door closed; and the visitor turned gravely, to where on the distant ridge tree leaves still glowed. 'The air is good here,' he said, as if remarking the fact for the very first time. 'It's not the air of England.'

She followed again, round to the driver's door. He stepped up on to the running board and swung inside. He pushed the window back and paused, as if still summoning thought. Then he nodded. 'The state of being and yet not being,' he said. 'The War is over; but nothing can really end. So everything becomes its own Nirvana.' He drummed his fingers on the wheel rim. 'You knew that already though,' he said. 'It was only us who needed the guns so badly.' He reached to press a starter button. The engine fired raggedly, settled to a steady beat. 'Thank you,' he said simply. 'Thank you very much.'

Kaeti stepped back. She said, 'Goodbye.'

The air was cooling, now the sun had all but gone. She walked to the middle of the little track, stood rubbing her upper arms, watching the vehicle as it moved away. A hundred yards off, its tail lights came on like an afterthought. Then it was gone, blended with blueness, faded from sight along the narrow way that still stretched dim and empty. She ran back then, picked up the plastic bag. She hurried through the little museum, where now were iron shadows; straddled her bicycle, turned a last time to stare. A slip of moon was showing; but the western sky was bright. Against it, empty now, was the rising swell of land; and dimly seen, the outline of a man who stared, out of the Salient toward the north. She watched a moment longer, then pulled at the latch of the gate. She pushed off with her sneakers, freewheeled away stiff-legged down the slope.

Richard Thornley

Casualty

RICHARD THORNLEY was born in 1950 in the West Midlands. Cape and Picador published his first book, *Zig Zag*. The passage printed here, entitled 'Casualty', is an excerpt from his recently completed manuscript about the mixed blessings of living in America: *Attempts to Join Society*.

*I*t was like one of those hushed control rooms that television space-ships seem to go for. Where the atmosphere is constant. Where the girls drift round in next to nothing. Where no one ever says much to any other member of the crew, and they never get irritable. They look at large screens and wait for the next meteorite.

Maybe it was more like being at the zoo – in the Aquarium, amongst the hushed comment from the visitors before the ripple-less tanks. Again the steady atmosphere of the chamber. The soft light filtering through the water over the large, blinking fish that hang motionless as if set in glass and reduced to a work of art; while the tiny bright minnows dart only according to some preconceived pattern.

Here was Bob, suspended in the tranquillity of the natal unit, obese with stagnation and contentment. And Peter having come back from the outside, from the basement, restlessly observing these creatures move to and fro behind the thick plate glass. He was searching for a brick. He found the atmosphere debilitating.

'If I stay here another two weeks, I'll die here.'

'There's worse places to die,' was Bob's comment, 'you only have to go down three floors to get packaged up.'

They were sitting in the staffroom towards the end of the day, seventeen deliveries under their belts and waiting for a late dropper.

'What's wrong with the woman?' Peter looked at his watch.

'We couldn't take her in the afternoon rush; they gave her some drugs to hold it back. Maybe they went over the dose . . .'

'Can't they give her some speed or something?' Bob rested his eyes on the television. 'You're not getting bored?' Peter continued to nibble at him.

'Nope.' Bob brushed him away. 'I'm going to get the sax up here and start practising. I've got the time and the place to do it; and I'm being paid. When I get out of here, I'll be the finest and richest sax-player in the country.' He grinned to himself.

The door opened and two nurses came in. Peter unwound from his slump and fetched some coffee. Bob made no move.

They were Sadie and Carol, they shared an apartment. They were interested. They talked; or Carol did, sitting on the arm of a chair. Sadie smoked and paid some limited attention to the television.

Peter warmed to Carol. He made a play for her and got nowhere. She was determined on Bob, hence their visit out of the blue. Bob was at his most indifferent, ignoring her and dealing himself out as a tramp. To keep things going, Peter gave up trying to force himself on Carol and swung over to take her side in the assault on Bob. There wasn't anything they could do. Bob didn't want to be disturbed, and Peter ended up talking about nothing in an artificial way. Carol was attractive. The whole conversation was pointless.

He talked to the other girl, Sadie, the second best. She didn't care, but she wasn't going to be condescended to. She flung her blandness back at him. He flirted with her, she responded carelessly.

It was Bob who killed it. Carol kept nagging at him until he flicked his eyes over her body and snapped at her.

'Do you want to get laid?'

She walked out of the room. Peter offered to take Sadie home in an hour, when his shift wound down. She said no, she would go with Carol, but she asked him to look in later for a coffee or a bourbon. It was arranged.

Bob was so touchy that Peter didn't ask him any questions. The mother came through with the kid soon afterwards; Peter cleared up and prepared to leave. Bob pulled on a cigarette. He asked Peter to apologize to Carol; it had been the only way to get rid of her. He was aiming to be self-sufficient at the moment and he wanted it known. He wasn't interested in her. His apologies. Not that it would break Carol's heart, she couldn't find it difficult to get hold of a man. Peter left him alone.

He bought some wine and went round to see the two girls, who lived in an up-market apartment block in the centre of town. They had both been married and were now separated, Carol living high off the alimony while Sadie made good money out of her senior position in the hospital. He wanted to end up in bed with Carol but she left the room soon after he arrived. After an hour's readjustment and the rest of the wine, Sadie and he went into her bedroom and screwed each other for whatever they had. At three in the morning she felt that he should leave and he went out of the door as she was clearing away the wine glasses.

*

Peter was back upstairs in the natal unit at eight the next morning with a sour taste in his mouth and even less enthusiasm for the routine. He pushed the mop over the floor and showed three fathers their products, he argued with Bob about nothing at all. He wanted out and, although last night probably left no openings, he waited for the phone to ring. The hours dragged on. He called the physiotherapy department at lunch break. Sadie was at lunch. He slammed the phone down and went to the canteen.

She was sitting with Carol and two other nurses at a corner table, eating a salad and drinking coffee. He approached. Sadie smiled and went on eating. Carol told him to pull up a chair. He fetched a hamburger and settled down at their table.

He couldn't handle four girls in a group; and they talked nursing, about which he knew nothing. Occasionally Carol would let herself out of the conversation and ask Peter about the natal unit or how he was enjoying it in America, but it was hard going, even tense. Peter wondered what he was doing there. If Sadie was listening in, she gave no sign of it. What the hell ... thought Peter, glancing at her.

Carol flirted with him, but she was only trying him out, probably keeping him away from her friend, and she went back to the group for a discussion on vertebrae. Peter realized that he was flogging a dead horse. They were girls in tryst, it was obvious. If he blew it, they would all turn to face him; if he stood up to leave, they would have their fun giggling about men and last night's lay. He stayed put, smoked a cigarette and picked up whatever scraps of interest Carol deigned to throw down for him. He was coming to hate her.

Sadie went across to fetch another cup of coffee. The other two nurses continued the medical bulletin, Carol was offering to let him talk about England. He couldn't find anything to say. He looked over at Sadie's back. She was twenty-eight and a head nurse in the physiotherapy department. She was medium height, pleasant, she had medium-length, light brown hair; she was sometimes pretty and she had a good sense of humour. The next-to-nothing uniform did a lot for Carol, but nothing for her. He warmed to her.

He looked back at Carol, trying to remember her last question and searching for something general to say in reply. He was stuck. Carol watched him, summing him up, and he floundered.

'Sadie's my best friend, she's lovely.' Carol eyed him. He nodded.

They relaxed. Peter had had interviews before. They were only unnerving when you didn't know that you were being interviewed. He assembled some views on England and the natal unit and New York, during which time Sadie returned and sat down, listening to him with half an ear and asking him if he could let her have one of his cigarettes. It was still non-committal when their break ended and they returned to work, Sadie wishing him a good day and saying how she'd probably see him around the hospital.

'She's shy.' Carol was the last to leave. 'You treated her badly yesterday. She's not crying out for a man, she's not nineteen.'

'*I* treated *her* badly?' He glared at Carol. 'I didn't even get time for a coffee last night . . .'

'That was balling, baby; it cost you a bottle of wine. You took her out of charity. Just don't do it again. Please? It's depressing for a lady, and Sadie is a lady.'

Peter followed her down the canteen to the door. Carol turned suddenly. 'And that goes for me too. I don't enjoy having her sleeping next to a guy who spreads his eyes over me.'

'Fuck you.'

'You won't.' Carol held the door open. Peter smiled at her. She hadn't decided whether or not to be friendly. Then she accepted it.

'I like Sadie,' he said.

'I'll tell her.' They wandered down the corridor. 'What's going on with Bob?' she asked him.

'I don't know,' Peter answered, 'nothing seems to interest him. He wants it that way. Do you want me to promote you like you just promoted Sadie?' He smiled; it didn't reach her.

'No,' she said.

'Do you know him well?' Peter guessed.

'I heard that he was down.' She avoided any history. 'It's a small town when you've lived here for more than a year. You appreciate people you took for granted when you first arrived. Maybe we'll be seeing you.' She went.

Peter took the elevator, pondering. He mentioned her to Bob.

'Yeah, rich bitches; they're all full of shit.' Bob let the screen door swing closed on the problem.

He called Sadie at four o'clock and asked her if she was doing anything that night.

'I'm cooking dinner. Are you vegetarian?'

'No. Am I invited?'

'Nine-thirty.'

'Good.'

'Work hard.' The phone went down.

He arrived at nine forty-five with another bottle of wine. The security guard checked his name against the list of admittables; he walked past the dusty rubber plants and hatstand ashtrays, glancing up at the camera which also kept an eye on things. Sadie was well protected.

She had changed and had scattered a very light cosmetic round her eyes.

Carol was also casual – under a writhing, serpentine hairstyle and flowing silk dress. It would have been breath-taking but there was something suspicious about the package deal, maybe the sun shone too brightly out of her eyes or the sky was too blue. Sadie drifted in and out of the kitchen while Carol, still in the brochure, entertained him over cigarettes and drinks. Her date arrived ten minutes later; he was straight out of the blue blue sky. He was the sort of person who made dinner-party conversation effortless, or redundant. Peter gathered that he was a disc jockey on the radio. If they'd given him a television chat show, they could have cut the budget by sixty per cent. He didn't need any guests, guests wouldn't have got a word in edgeways.

He perched on the couch for five minutes while everyone acclimatized themselves to his authority. Then he moved to the rug and snorted a vast line of coke, he rolled a couple of joints, he led the way to the table and took a forkful of everything. And all this time he talked. 'English, yeah? Working with the nurses here, yeah? Doing the States, yeah? . . .' and he knew Peter off pat. Peter didn't even have to agree with him, the guy was in so much agreement with himself. He broadcast to them the whole way through the meal. The words flurried into ideas, the ideas banked into deep drifts. Communication seized up. Only Carol poked her voice out into the blizzard, and the blizzard paused just to take account of the obstacle, and then it swept her away.

Peter sagged forward with his elbows on the table when they left to go dancing. The voice hung in the air after the swirl of silk and the shutting of the door. Silence tiptoed in and pulled up a cautious chair next to Peter. He became aware of its presence.

'Do you ever have that feeling . . .' he looked up at Sadie, 'that you are boring, that you don't fit into society, that the world pounds past you without worrying where it puts its feet? Does he dance like that? Does he ever get a chance to play any music on his programme?'

'Not you as well ...' Sadie complained. 'Cool out. Don't let it become contagious.'

She pulled her legs up under her and knelt on the chair to roll a joint. The room slowly settled. She turned off one of the lights, putting some Satie on the stereo. A pianist quietly tapped out the composer's madness. Sadie listened, straight-backed and impassive.

'Not many people could dance to *that*,' she said, as the record ended. 'It reminds me of the bone classes when I was a student, jiggling the skeleton around.'

She talked mainly to herself, with a nervous smile on the end of her mouth for Peter. It was, in a sense, their first evening together. The night before was well out of her mind. The music was severe and the talker had exhausted both of them. The only time Sadie alluded to their bedding was when she raised an eyebrow and asked if he wanted any coffee; she smiled. 'It's the least I could offer.'

The labour was left to the coffee-machine and she showed him the apartment, the mess of Carol's room, the prints from Europe in the hallway; and her bedroom, now dauntingly clear of debris, a rug completely covering the bed from pillows to floor, a night-dress laid across the centre. Her nurse's shift was on a hanger, dangling from the wardrobe door; there were medical journals stacked by the side of her reading-light, nothing personal other than a few cosmetics over near the window and a picture of her family which Peter was sure hadn't been there the night before. The room had been arranged to make a point, it was stated clearly to him.

She picked the picture up and brought it out into the lounge. This room was more homely, though it had been the other way round last night. Carol had used the lounge as a backdrop for her portrait, Sadie moved amongst the lamps and chairs with the sureness of a cat. The souvenirs and ornaments were obviously hers.

'Did you live here when you were married?' Peter asked, as she arranged the photograph on the writing-desk.

'I thought I swept the place out pretty good ...' she didn't turn round. She didn't seem to know what to do with him.

'Rich husband?' Peter peered at a miniature over the false fireplace.

'So-so. I bought everything off him. I do all right on my own, buster.'

'Buster who?' Peter had finished looking round her house and wanted to catch her eye. It wasn't forthcoming. He felt that the party was over, but there was still the coffee.

'Shall I flip the record?'

'No. Not unless you want to hear it.' She surprised him. 'It's cold music. There's some B.B. King down there somewhere.'

He searched for it while she went through to get the coffee. He found it, and the needle lowered itself. There was a fast track and her foot tapped out the tempo.

Then the maestro started on 'The thrill has gone ... the thrill has gone away ...' Sadie set a tray in front of him and busied herself with it, cross-legged on the rug. The song poured over them, the man reached far into his chagrin and dragged it out into the light. Sadie with the coffee-pot in her hand and her mouth turned down like a weary old bin-hound. Peter laughed. She took a cigarette off him and smoked it.

'What about the dishes?'

'That's for Carol,' she said.

'Will she do them?'

'Sure she'll do them. Or she'll have them in her bed tomorrow night. I'm no pet dog. I'm a great cook.' She eyed him for the dues.

'You are. Thanks.'

'That's okay.'

'What else do you do?'

'I'm a good lover, aren't I?'

'Yes?' He was taken aback.

'You'd better believe it.'

'Why?'

'Because that's how I paid for my life.'

'Oh.'

Peter knew she wanted to go on, but she hadn't made up her mind and the silence couldn't be covered by slurping coffee for very long, or listening to her several attempts at striking a match.

'Is it still like that?' he asked her.

'I had to get free of my husband; I had to get this apartment.' Sadie told the story monotonously, using her hands, building it up brick by brick like she wanted to make sure the wall was solid. It was all grey, though every now and then she would plaster it with some lurid poster to see how he reacted. It was a dull story, no anger or sympathy; and she was very safe, looking at him from behind this wall. She had constructed her life out of calling-cards, the late-night massage service, the throat, the body and the warm, sticky oblivion for a hundred men on her taste buds. She started with the car and finished with the apartment. One night she was in a rush and didn't have time to change out of her nurse's gear. The man liked it. It gave him some spice.

Then she stopped, and went to lie on a beach for a month. She saw the need for some compromise and a friend. Carol helped out.

The coffee was finished, the stereo had turned itself off a long time ago.

'What are you doing tomorrow night?' Peter asked her.

'I'm going out.'

'Fair enough.' He thanked her for the dinner. She picked up the house-phone and told the guard he was coming down. She saw him to the door, tired. She averted her lips and they hugged before he walked down the corridor to the elevator.

'Goodnight.' Peter walked towards the guard. He nodded and unlocked the door. He went back to his crime magazines, Peter to the hospital.

He stumbled through the next day at work and wanted to get out on the town as soon as he could. Bob was becoming annoyed at covering for him.

'One more night,' Peter insisted.

'Okay, but if the supervisor comes on heavy then I'm not going to screw myself up with excuses.'

'Yeah.'

'You want to quit?' Bob looked at him.

'The money's too good.'

Bob snorted in disgust.

'I'll take a day off, and I'll cut back to doing just the one shift. Do you want to cut back?'

'Nope. I've got nothing better to do.' Bob shook his head.

'Nor have I.'

'What about Sadie?'

'I don't think so.'

Bob flipped up and down the scales on the sax. 'So you're going to sit in Jake's all night and get drunk?'

'Yes.'

'You'd better take the keys to the apartment. I'll see you in the morning.' He went back to the sax.

Peter eased into the drunk slowly, not even keen on the idea nor feeling any particular taste for the means of doing it. The beer was lousy, the Daniels was too quick, the cocktails too much paraphernalia. If he drank Laird's he felt guilty about leaving Bob up in the unit alone. And the amount of orange juice they put in the tequila made it sickly.

It was out of this indecision that the drunk arrived. It crept up unnoticed and went past him, throttle wide open, dragging him along in its slipstream. He had nothing to say to anyone though conversation came and went with whoever happened to sit on the stool next to him. He was English, people wanted to talk about something serious, something comparative. As he got more drunk, it exasperated him. What do you think of England? Shit. What do you reckon to the States? Shit.

Bob's old date, Chestnut, came in on the arm of a new man, and Peter found it even more difficult to talk with an acquaintance than to a stranger. They dissolved away from him into a far corner of the bar. Peter stuck to his glass, blindly.

Late into the night, he recognized a flash of blond hair. He turned unsteadily. The Kid was over by the door, feeding the cigarette machine for a packet of Kools. Peter was glad enough to see him. The Kid walked over, peeling the cellophane off the pack; Peter ordered him a beer.

'What's going on?'

'I got back from a club in the city. We're doin' real good. Got a new keyboard man.' The Kid lit a cigarette and reached over the stool to get rid of the match. He nodded at Peter. 'Hear you two are down at the hospital.'

'I'm drunk,' said Peter.

'Yeah? I don't drink that much. I can't. I got a screwed-up liver. I like smoking grass better; it's good for your head.'

'Right.'

'Yeah ... well ... I gotta get back and see my old lady, stop her bitching. If you show at one of the gigs, I can get you a couple of freeloaders' tickets.'

'I'll be seeing you.'

'Bring Bob along. Maybe it would do him some good to get back into music again.'

'Sure.'

And that was it. The Kid left. Peter was too drunk to talk, or even to suggest going back to his place for a smoke.

He lit another cigarette out of nothing else to do, and couldn't handle it. He drank half the Kid's beer and caught himself in favour of letting his head go down on the bar; to sleep, to sleep.

He pulled himself off the stool and plodded his feet towards the exit, surprised and proud that his body was following. The barman called after him, something about his cigarettes; he waved a hand vaguely and stumbled into the night air.

It was a way to walk, a long way. Peter sighed.

He leant against the wall but realized that if he sat down he wouldn't get up again until morning. He wondered if he should make himself sick. Dialogue between brain and stomach. It got tedious and he felt himself sleeping, the weight on his legs was terrific, he wondered that the tarmac took it. His shirt scraped against the wall.

There were other people coming out of Jake's, a long way away. Peter stuck his hands in his pockets and looked as if he was waiting for a bus. But there were no buses. He stumbled round the corner. He wondered if he'd make it. There was nothing to sing.

His boots were too heavy. The hedge and the grass looked strange in the night-light, motionless.

He yawned, and becoming more conscious of where he was, he felt more sober, or less incapably drunk. He walked on. It came into his head that he should go to see Sadie, talk things over with her, help her out a bit. He laughed out loud at this alcoholic shifting of responsibilities; the moment she opened her mouth, he would go to sleep. She was out, anyway.

Could he piss here? One of these wooden houses, behind the hedge. Which wasn't tall enough to hide him from the road. He ducked down, and listened for the silence. Only the roar in his ears.

He got it out and bent over it, muttering to it and coaxing it. Cursing it as the pain in his back became apparent. Or was he going to be sick? Is that why he was here?

He looked up at the sky, where there was nothing further than the glow from the streetlamps, no moon, no stars, and the road with nothing on it. He slipped backwards and looked down again to balance. He collided with the hedge. He laughed at himself, annoyed underneath. He would walk on, that was better.

He was going past her place anyway. It was a tall building, he couldn't remember what floor, but there was a light on one of the floors, in one of the rooms. It would be hers. Things are made that way.

Peter took several deep breaths and wondered if he could handle it. Shit, he could wish her a good evening over the housephone, joke a little, remind her that he existed, that he was a late night creature like she was, the kind of person who was disinterestedly friendly.

The guard was at his desk, looking at Peter through the glass entrance, with his revolver laid out on the magazines.

Peter tapped. The guard looked at him and then at his watch. Peter went through some mimicry about wanting to get inside. The guard came round the desk with the gun in his hand, eyeing Peter while he turned the key in the door. He let Peter in.

'Who for?'

Peter gave the name and his own. The guard kept an eye on him while he telephoned. 'It's gettin' on to be late, mister, and you've had a lot of liquor. You sure you don't want me to call the lady up in the morning?'

'No, she might be expecting me.' Peter now didn't believe a word of it. The light was dazzling him; he might just have the energy to leave his name. The guard hung on the phone.

'Miss Sadie? This is George, ma'am. There's someone down here in the lobby for you. It's a quarter of three, ma'am. That's right. I will . . .'

'Thank you, George.' The guard handed the phone over to Peter who didn't have a brain in his head. 'Hi . . .'

There was no answer.

'Are you awake? Sadie?'

'Yes. I'm awake. I was just going to bed.'

'Oh.'

George turned away and sat back down in his chair, utterly indifferent, noting down the time of the call on a printed chart. In case he got killed? Peter watched him blearily. Surely the killer wouldn't be so dumb as to leave the time sheet lying there for the police.

'Can I help you?' Sadie's voice.

'I was out on the town, I got drunk. It was a mistake. I'm sorry. What've you been doing?'

She was silent again.

'What?' Peter asked.

'Okay, hand me over to George.'

Peter gave George the phone, having no idea what was going to happen, thinking possibly that now was the time to bow out and make a last effort to get back to Bob's. The apartment, he realized, was the other direction from Jake's Barn.

'Twenty minutes . . . I'll do that, ma'am.' George hung the phone up. 'You got in; I sure as hell hope you're goin' to behave yourself up there.'

'What floor is it?' Peter was elated.

'Four.'

'I'll take the stairs; I need the exercise.'

'You jus' take the elevator, it's right here.'

George came round the desk and pressed all the right buttons for

Peter. He arrived on the fourth floor without having said goodnight to George. He said it in the corridor, and thank you, George.

He found the geography and pressed the buzzer to her apartment, falling in love with her, her night-dress and the robe over it. She looked at him.

'You *are* drunk.'

'I know.' Peter leant in the hallway.

'Very?'

'Yeah.'

'George is going to phone through in fifteen minutes to check out that you don't have any ideas.'

He laughed. 'I might collapse but I haven't got any ideas.'

'I'll make you some coffee. Why don't you sit in the lounge? The lights are a little bright in the kitchen.'

He put his arm over her shoulder, but she pulled away and walked bare-footed to the kitchen.

'Thanks, Sadie.'

'In the lounge,' she called to remind him.

The cushions were on the carpet. Peter stretched out and took his boots off, then sat up to try to restore his consciousness.

'Where's your date?' he mumbled. He cleared his throat. 'Where's your date?'

'I stayed in tonight,' she came through with some black instant coffee, 'Carol went out and I wanted to be on my own to read a book.'

'*Doctor Zhivago*.' Peter mumbled.

'Very funny.' She smiled at his state.

'Not bad,' Peter sipped at the coffee, 'for the time of night, not bad.' He felt himself going again. He put the coffee cup on the carpet. He asked her: 'Sadie, I want to go to bed.'

She looked at him from over the top of her bunched-up legs and considered.

'All right.'

And then he virtually went to sleep where he sat, except that she pulled him out of his well of booze and took off most of his clothes and put him in her bed. Then she phoned down to George and went to sleep next to him, back to back.

She pulled him out again next morning. 'You're working. I've called the hospital to tell them you'll be in late, and it's okay, you don't have to worry about it. Take a bath and a shave. There's a razor which I use on my legs, and a toothbrush ... wake up ... dammit ...' She shook him and shook him.

Peter was still drunk, with something skittering frivolously over his nervous system. She told him to hurry, because the bath was running. Peter groaned from the hangover.

'You can take me out and buy me a few drinks this evening.' She surprised him again.

'You've decided?'

'Yes, why, haven't you?' She busied through to turn the water off in the bathroom.

'When did you decide?' he called. She put her head round the door.

'I think it was when ... just after you'd been sick over the side of the bed, and I had to check whether or not you were going to choke and kill yourself. Medical reasons. And you looked so damn happy while you were doing it, I thought maybe you should pay for me to get as drunk as that.'

Peter winced.

'Oh, we'll find something to do. I'll walk up and down on your spine or something. Anyway, it's my turn to listen to you. If you like.' She came back to lie on the bed next to him, with her hand holding up her chin.

'What time do you get off work?'

'It's Saturday, dopey. It's the weekend; no work, brother.' Her lips rested on his shoulder, she bit lightly.

'Shall I get Sunday off?' Peter dropped the words into her ear.

'Yes.'

'What about Carol?'

'Oh are you that much of a man?' She swung her head back and opened her eyes, wide and playful.

'No.'

'Carol didn't come in last night. If she doesn't come in on Friday night, she's gone for the weekend. One day falling in love, one day making love, one day falling out of love. She sets her hair and she goes to work on Monday. She's a kid.'

'You're joking?'

'I admire it.'

'Did she ever have anything going with Bob?'

Peter propped his shoulder up with his elbow and traced a finger over her breast.

'Ah, now, Bob ... mm ...' Sadie retreated.

'Ah, mmm, what?' Peter followed her out of the door, girded about with the sheet.

'The dark and mysterious Bob ... do you want the bath or shall

I let the water out? Take a bath. What about eight-thirty this evening?'

'I get off at midnight.'

'*Who* does? You do a double shift?'

'Unless I can get it changed somehow.'

Sadie pouted at him. 'Shame . . .'

'I'll get it changed. I'll get a lot changed.'

She followed him into the bathroom. 'I know, you're going to pull your whole life together.'

'That's right,' Peter stepped into the water and knelt down, 'I met this girl . . .' Sadie laughed at him and flicked the soap into the bath.

'And you were so drunk each time you saw her that the only thing you can remember about her was her meat.'

Peter was shocked, even dizzy what with the hangover. He pulled the soap off the bottom of the bath. They were both embarrassed.

'That's not true. That's not what I remember. That's not what I'm looking at.' Peter spoke quietly, and started soaping himself that they both might forget it.

'One boob? A leg?' Sadie attempted to make light of it all and keep things running, but they still were hanging there. She scratched his shoulder softly. 'Maybe not,' she said, 'I make good coffee, how did we start on this and can we forget it . . .' she ran quickly.

'Eight-thirty,' he said.

'I'll look forward to it.' She stood up to leave him.

'So what about Bob and Carol?' Peter started washing.

'No,' she said, 'a girl doesn't talk about her friend's affairs, not in my book. So don't ask me about it.'

Free of the hangover, Peter transferred himself from the hospital to Sadie. He organized it with Bob, and had it stamped by the administration office after lunch. He would work six days a week in the natal unit, and only one shift per day. Bob contacted another musician and suggested that he took on the night shift. Money and rehearsal time fit together cleanly. The administration were grateful for the clarity of the plan, Bob nodded at the convenience, and Peter was just glad to be out of the place for a while.

At 8.30 even George smiled as Peter walked into the foyer, showered and cleaned up for the night. Peter handled his own elevator, up to the fourth and along the familiar corridor to where Sadie was glamorous in holding the door open.

'Did George let you know I was on the way up?'

'It's eight-thirty, isn't it? We arranged for eight-thirty, I didn't think you'd forget.' She was happily reassured by his arrival, she had made an effort with her hair and clothes and she was now a bit nervous at the give-away. Peter made a mistake.

'You shouldn't have bothered to get all dressed up,' he said.

'Well I did bother, so there! What's wrong with it? Don't you like it?' She walked in front of him down the hallway to the lounge.

'That's not what I meant. I got changed as well.'

'I noticed. I was just going to tell you how nice you looked.'

'Thank you. So do you.'

'Thank you.'

She poured him a bourbon and avoided his eyes when she gave it to him. She lit a cigarette, pulling at it furiously, marching round the room, rearranging objects oppressively, disturbing it. Peter caught her hand. They walked across to the window and calmed down a little. He brushed her hair out of the way and kissed her lightly on the back of the neck. She let her body relax against his.

'Where are we going?' she asked.

'Oh, I don't know ...' Peter murmured romantically, 'Let's take it slowly and see where it leads us.' He put his arm round her and looked out over the city.

'I mean, to eat.'

'Ah ...'

She was shaking with suppressed laughter against his side. She laughed her pleasure away down the room, picking up a light wrap to throw over her shoulders. 'Come on, then, let's see where it leads us. But let's take a cab, I can't walk very far in these shoes.'

It was a disaster, the restaurant. Saturday night, the married couples out on the town, the uniform cooking, the supermarket music, the open-plan, back-to-back seating, the subtle neon lighting, the buzz of formal conversation from people who knew each other too well to find anything to say.

They had a wonderful time, they got slightly drunk and laughed at each other and their surroundings. Sadie had a great sense of humour, Peter of ridicule. It was like getting married in Las Vegas, it was one big success story, right down through the pre-packaged French fries to the disgusting coffee. They even managed an argument about who should pay the bill, each of them prostrating themselves before overwhelmingly good reasons for financial sacrifice.

'I'm a nurse, I make more money, right?'

'I've got my pride as a worker.'

'You want to be a slave?'

'Don't be an idiot.'

And an argument about liberation and what each of them was supposed to be getting out of it, an argument about relative national wealth.

'I'm staying at your apartment, so I'll pay for the dinner.'

'You think you're staying at my apartment? You take that for granted?'

'No?' Peter worried. They played around with the inevitability of this. 'Well, you pay for yours and I'll pay for mine,' he offered. 'Don't be so greedy with your independence.'

'I don't like being kept.'

'I haven't got you.'

Peter put the dollar bills on top of the check and went to the lavatory. Sadie put the dollar bills in his coat pocket and paid with a card. Peter found them the next day and left them in her writing-desk. Sadie sent them up to the natal unit in an envelope; Peter gave them to George. Sadie had Bob take them back; Peter refused them. Bob got bored with it and pushed the money into his own pocket.

All of this took three days. That Saturday night, Sadie and Peter got back to the apartment and made love alongside the pile of crumpled clothes which were left to fend for themselves on the bedroom floor, night to day to night again. Carol appeared on Sunday and recognized the couple's wish to be left alone. They heard the radio coming from her bedroom.

Peter slowed into sleep early on Sunday evening, Sadie on his arm. They understood very little about each other. Their good humour and pleasure enabled them to steer clear of any doubts, their inquisitiveness was mostly physical. It was a weekend romance with possibilities best left unmentioned.

Both of them found the other awake very early on Monday morning at a strange hour, with the light on and not a sound from the street or the building. They whispered. The depth of the calm was unusual for America. She said that she only expected him to stay with her for a week, maybe two.

'Why?'

'Because my life is at the hospital, and when the strike ends you'll go on somewhere else. Won't you?'

'Mm ...' He lay along the bed on his front, his hands flat under his chin, looking at the wall. Sadie meandered one finger over his spine. He supposed she was right, but he stirred in annoyance and wondered where she thought he'd go.

'Wherever you want.'

She started to rub his back slowly, her hands spreading out and arriving at his shoulders. She sat up beside him and felt the muscles running from his neck, she felt that he was tense.

'I wouldn't worry,' she said, 'some people find what they want to do early on, and if you can't find anything like that then it's best to travel around and try everything.' She squeezed the muscle affectionately.

'And you don't mind?' he asked.

'Since I was married, I don't like keeping people for more than a week or two.'

'You don't give people a chance. Or yourself.'

'I know what I want; I don't take chances.'

She sat on him and let talcum powder fall over his back. She put the container down on the floor and started to massage.

'That's nice.'

'It's my work. I don't get much chance to do it now; everything's electric, or hydro. Relax. I'm only going to rub you down. Your spine is all right for your age.'

'Thank you.'

She had a smile on her lips when he looked back at her.

She worked in silence. It was very pampering, very tranquil; she was strong and fully involved in the rhythm of her own fingers and arms. She took him away, dormant, for long periods of time, removing herself as a person, only the slightest rise and fall from her thighs as she reached for his shoulders. His mind went back over her, through other women and returned to Sadie.

'Are you sure you're not being defensive?' he ventured.

'You're very lovable; I'm sure that I *am* being defensive.' She said this without pretension and without guile, letting him know that she wouldn't change. 'That's the way I am. So.' She unpinned her leg and sat back on the top of his thigh.

'A whole number,' she whispered drowsily when she was curled damp against him an hour before dawn, and 'I love you.'

Occasionally they got that close. But then, like two security-conscious governments, they still had the plan. One week, maybe two. However much she laughed at herself, she rationed out the spontaneity in a miserly fashion, watching from her tower for any dissident emotions. Whether it was that she didn't trust him, or he didn't trust himself, he couldn't find out.

Maybe it was his fault, he was obviously angling for something to keep him interested. He had transferred all his energy from the hospital in a rush; and she, neatly and firmly, handed it back to him. She didn't want to be flattened by it.

Or possibly it was the intrusion of the working week, Monday to Friday. It didn't exhaust her, but she organized herself around it and it was cosy. She liked being organized; she had none of the need for some desperate leisure as an antithesis, she didn't like chaos, she moved securely in her own world. Sometimes he felt like a tourist; she dispelled this easily, but it was still there every now and then.

She drove them both to the hospital each morning; she would give him a quick kiss and always the 'Work hard'. She preferred to wait to see him after their shifts rather than meet him downstairs at midday for lunch. She never said as much, but Monday and Tuesday when he went into the canteen, she was at the same table in the same company and there were overtones of the first lunchtime meeting, Carol doing most of the talking. He got on all right with Carol, but he could see that Sadie was tense and that he was only her lover when they were alone. She wanted to reserve him for that; she accepted that he could share that compartment for the time being, she was happy with it. Beyond that, there was to be no progression.

She was aware that things were uneasy in the apartment when Carol was around, and she used this intrusion to remind him that their affair was not limitless. It wasn't indifference that ruled her; she was simply determined that nobody should get hurt. They took a midweek night out at Bob's apartment; her idea, Peter hated the place. She didn't like it, but she made the best of it, warming the untouched rooms by her presence and succeeding in making him feel at home there for the first time. He understood that she was glad to be able to provide him with an alternative centre of gravity, one other than herself, and that she was setting herself up for the painless departure.

One week or two? It might as well be one, though they were both obviously growing more fond of each other, Sadie tentative, Peter withholding any pressure out of respect for the way she had built up her independence.

He heard on Thursday that the strike was to end at the weekend, and his attachment to the hospital would be over. She knew as well, but she didn't mention it. The decision would have to be taken too soon, there would have to be a reason for staying. It was unfortunate. She wasn't a hard woman, not untouchable, not resigned, not careless, not cold, not playing any games. A lot of nots, with someone not knowing whether to struggle out of them. She wasn't dead; just the opposite, she was very much alive.

They avoided the subject without much difficulty, they settled on a week without saying anything to each other. Thursday and Friday were slow evenings, tender. Saturday they might have been cynical, offhand, or religious about it all. He decided to take her into New York so that they could drift apart in the lulling cacophony of the city.

He was depressed on the Saturday shift, not that the blood and the babies and the fathers caused him any departure pains. Life would go on without scab labour. Bob and he split some beer after collecting their last wage packet; Bob was working Sunday, he wished Peter a good time in the city and figured on seeing him in front of the TV set on Monday evening. He told Peter to clear out an hour after their lunch break. Peter walked out of the basement exit and up the hill past the garbage crusher without taking a deep breath.

Sadie didn't want to go into New York. They were both full of the sense that it was one of their last evenings together. They didn't have any plan. Peter insisted that they set off without any plan in mind, that they should walk around the city and do whatever took their fancy, letting themselves be open to the surroundings and the people and the choice of entertainment. Sadie conceded reluctantly. It ran against her grain. She armed herself with two packets of cigarettes and a determination to see it through. The car was out of the game; she called up a friend and arranged to leave it in a high-security underground automobile bunker just off the Park on 57th, where the office took her driving licence with the photograph on it and her keys. So the car was safe. And the car meant a lot to Sadie. She didn't mind walking.

They ambled slowly down through the midtown area, zigzagging over from Fifth to Second Avenue and back again in time for Grand Central Station, not so much interested in the buildings as the people, and not so much interested in them as in the whirlygig of colour and impression. It was a lazy stroll. They took a coffee and a beer at some place on 42nd street and decided to go on down into Gramercy Park to pick up the subway on 28th if they got that far without succumbing to the humidity.

The buildings came down to meet them as they got into the thirties. They were a couple of blocks past 34th Street, beginning to feel tired, the evening was starting to fade. Peter glanced both ways at the lights and elected to head east. Sadie wanted to stick on Lexington, but he persuaded her that it wasn't interesting. They turned east.

This street was strangely artificial, as though someone had taken the trouble to assemble a collection of caricatures for social observation.

It was probably a poor street, it didn't look as though the Sanitation Department visited too often. It couldn't have been very dangerous for there was a cop car parked halfway down, and one cop chatted easily to the passers-by. It wasn't a ghetto like Third Avenue or Harlem.

Sadie hung on to his arm, which gave them their own identity, for as far as he could see they were the only couple on the street. It would be a good two hundred yards to stroll. They sauntered. It was a people street.

They threaded their way through the garbage in front of four old blacks sitting on beer crates, they were passed by younger, sharper blacks on their way into Harlem for the night; they stopped to watch a delivery driver arguing with a line of waiting cars, he had a good command of the language, the irate drivers wound up their windows and blasted their horns. The trucker ignored them; Peter and Sadie drifted on, away from the noise. Two Jews argued fervently under their hats, an old and a young; spicy smells distracted Peter to a delicatessen where he bought a huge torpedo, stuffed with meat and peppers, Sadie laughed at him.

A smart hippy lady strutted towards them and disappeared up a flight of steps; there was a small, grimy bookshop and a bar buried underneath the house at the side of it. A black hooker paused against the wall to touch up her hair, while a drunken failure negotiated the steps, searching for her fee. She smiled at him. A businessman, rich enough to feel out of place, kept a steady direction and a preoccupied expression on his face. A guy in a mohair suit looked scornfully up at the sky while a punk held a hand out to him, jabbering his angle; the guy put on his shades as Peter and Sadie passed. All these people they saw. Peter wiped his mouth on the paper and threw the remaining half of the torpedo in the direction of the trashcan, which swallowed it neatly. Style. Luck, said Sadie.

They came up to and passed the two cops and their car. They were now involved with an informer, who sat in the back seat, leaning forward, gesticulating. Peter caught his eye; a cop wound up the car window. The informer started again. A nondescript man with a brief-case bumped against Sadie and apologized, and went on ahead of them, those short American trousers flapping against the top of his ankles. Two kids in white basketball boots skipped in and out and around the pedestrians, bouncing nothing between them, to and fro; their ownership of the streets. Peter followed their progress, their mad dance as they weaved away past a big Italian lady with her arm under a sack of groceries, a youngster trailing along beside her, an old lady with a dog, a black activist, the back of the nondescript man – a paunchy guy in a white shirt, coming down the steps with a gun, pushing a woman away from him – it all froze, the people in front of his eyes.

The black activist, perhaps his mind naturally picked up on the wave of dangerous energy, had a split second to look up before he died, he just folded on to the pavement, the gun was going off again, the nondescript man was lying down and coughing blood over his briefcase. Peter saw. It was random. He threw Sadie into the side of the wall. The gun pointed at them, held in two hands, Peter couldn't move.

The gun switched, the guy turned away and picked out one of the kids. Shame, thought Peter, the kid screamed violently and ran his death into the side of a car. The guy's woman was once again hanging on to his arm. He shook her off and killed the black hooker who was on the other side of the street. It was a good shot; the drunk stared in disbelief. Peter couldn't move; people realized and started running; the groceries went down in the gutter; Peter knew he wouldn't get killed. There was a moment when the crowd took over, the guy was filled with indecision. The gun flickered from target to Peter to target. The Italian woman was shot in the leg. The gunman's energy was running out. Maybe it was the noise from the groceries. Peter was hit hard in the back and fell to the pavement. A cop knelt beside him, took aim, and shot the gunman in the chest.

Sadie was huddled behind a garbage can, one hand clutching the rim, weeping silently. The cop ran up the street to watch the gunman die over the railings. Peter knelt on the pavement, peaceful for a moment, until the screams of the world disturbed him.

He got to his feet. The nondescript man was injured, there was nothing he could do. For some reason, he walked forward and lifted the dead kid on to the bonnet of the car. This seemed to arrange things better. He looked at the kid and put his hand into the gore coming out of the chest, it was warm, he put a smear of it behind his ear. He wiped his hand against the car. He looked up. He was a long way from anywhere.

The cop-car arrived beside him. He recalled that it had just travelled fifty yards with its lights and sirens. He moved away from it. The blood on his hand was already drying and was like a thin rubber glove over his skin. He walked back to Sadie's body, her torment was wide-eyed and catatonic, she shrank away behind the garbage can. He pulled her out by the arm and looked at her. He slapped her twice, hard, across the face. Her eyes were dull.

'Sadie ... Sadie ...' he called. She wasn't there. He drew her close and whispered to her. 'Sadie ... listen ... you're alive. There are people who are hurt. It's your job, Sadie.'

She wasn't there; she was in shock. She was far gone. He took his hand off her back and tightened it round the handle to the garbage bin – he needed to feel something solid. Then he put the hand round his other wrist, clutching the flesh. It was all the same devoid material. An appalling fear reached for him. He knew that he was close to having exhausted his credit. Sadie's whole body started to shake and he held on to her. His guardian angel slipped quietly away; it left a cold smear, like a snail.

Peter knew his balance was being overdrawn, when he stood there confidently watching the psychopath pick his targets, watching the gun swing round at him, the barrel waver and turn away. He knew. He didn't need reminding. He wouldn't forget. He wasn't dumb. He was low on assets but he wasn't broke, not yet. He knew also that Sadie would have been shot when the gun came across, that the body hanging on to him would have been left uninhabited. The girl deserved better than fatality.

Slowly, painfully slowly, odd sobs ventured out and heaved up from her breast into the daylight, reasserting herself, cleaning her out. She cried. She howled once in anguish for everything and as the first ambulance arrived she picked herself up, told Peter to keep warm and moved across to see what she could do for the wounded. She asked him to keep hold of her purse.

They both followed the wounded and the dead to the hospital, their shirts covered in blood from the nondescript man, who might make it if they pumped enough plasma into him during his ambulance ride. Peter hadn't wanted to visit the hospital, but Sadie insisted and he let himself be taken care of, glad of the daze and the relaxation.

What else was there to do? You couldn't just stroll into a bar or a movie after having been in a scene like that, you needed some special surroundings to woo you through the clear-out impressions and surges of re-enactment. And the hospital would be the nearest thing to going home, for Peter as well as for her.

She showed her nurse's card and they sat in the staffroom over cups of tea and a pill, recovering their strength. The pill took over.

Peter sat in a corner, wrapped in a blanket, smoking cigarettes while the electricity in his mind flashed and crackled and finally subsided under the influence of the drug. He fused slowly with his exhaustion.

The news came through in jerks and snippets from the white-clad nurses wheeling in and out of the room.

Excluding the killer, three dead and two wounded.

Six shock cases.

The nondescript man was critical.

The killer had shot at the first five people he saw, his wife was under sedation. His wage packet had been stolen for the second week running, and he had lost his head. Police would take statements from anyone who wished to file an insurance complaint.

What? Against capitalism? File a complaint? Never. Against loneliness? Against a miserable job and a miserable wage? Against lack of self-respect? Desperation? Peter tittered. A lawsuit against God, he would sue God for everything the bastard had. Who would represent God? Wall Street. Would God win? Yes.

Peter didn't wish to file a complaint. Nor did Sadie. The drug was balmy. He could watch any movie over and over again. Sadie slept.

It was absurd how unimposing the experience was. They both felt tired, but mostly indifferent. For Peter it was too strange, for Sadie perhaps it merely confirmed what she had known about life outside her walls. They were exhausted and sluggish.

By midnight, they were out the other side. Their minds stirred restlessly and they were hungry. Their shirts were brought to them from the hospital laundry, they each took a shower.

Sadie didn't want to drive home just yet in case the effect of the drug, or the shooting, returned. They decided to have something to eat in the city and pick up the car later.

They called a cab and Sadie immediately chose their destination, not having any further desire to experiment. Peter played passenger, musing on his strange relationship with the dead kid. He had washed the blood off his neck in the shower. Sadie was silent, her head on his shoulder. She interrupted their daydreams.

'What's it like in England?'

'Boring.' Peter laughed at its attraction.

'Underneath.'

'Tea and boring.'

'Come on . . .' her head nudged him.

'It is. The country is geared for people between the ages of forty and fifty. There's no way round it. Until you reach that age, there's no point in staying there.'

'I might like it there.'

He failed to notice what she said, he was thinking for himself.

'You steal what you can. Otherwise you get static; and when you get to forty you become a cheerleader for some principle or other. Like death.'

'Did you live alone?' she asked.

'No; with another guy.'

'What does he do?'

'Him? Nothing. He's the only person I know who can do nothing successfully.'

'That's sad.'

'No, I don't mean that he isn't successful; I mean that he does nothing, successfully, with a lot of success.'

'How can you do that?' Sadie wondered.

'I don't know.'

'And you always steal what you can?'

'Not always.'

'Well,' she put her arms round him, 'I think you'd better go and steal something off California.'

The cab drew up outside a restaurant. Sadie was out first and paid. Peter shut the cab door and stood on the pavement. He looked up at the humiliating buildings, he lost himself for a moment. Sadie tugged at his arm and walked past him towards the restaurant. He caught her by the door.

'Sadie? Have I stolen anything off you?'

'No,' she smiled at him, 'you're not that skilful. This is America, remember? You can buy me dinner though, if you like.'

Even at one o'clock at night, the restaurant was crowded. It was one of those international spartan-cult places, all stripped wood and art posters, servers in long cotton dresses or blue jeans, a lot of dopey smiling and soft voices. There was only one place to sit and that was in the corner, opposite a fat man who was poking daintily at a teeny-weeny vegetarian salad.

Peter buried his head in the menu. He was hungry. He wanted three cheeseburgers and a couple of pints of beer. The menu would have made a rabbit's eyes light up, a squirrel would have been in seventh heaven, but it was the end of the road for carnivores. Peter scanned the menu again, and a third time. It seemed to be possible to pay ten dollars for a plate of raw cabbage and carrot, grown out of organic fertilizers. If he'd been walking along the side of the road fifty miles to the north, he could have pulled a whole meal out of the ground in a hundred yards. Peter looked at the rest of the customers – a bit of artificial nitrogen and iron and speed would have been a drop in the ocean of drugs.

'How would you like to order for the both of us, and a bottle of wine . . .' he left the solid problem to Sadie.

The great fat man opposite was chewing over his greenery, Peter expected to see a string of cud-juice hanging from his mouth. Two small, piggy eyes flicked over at him and must have read his disgust. Three chins wobbled and the mouthload sank down somewhere into the vast bulk. The pudgy hand reached out and squeezed a glass of water which it brought up to the lips. Once more the chins wobbled and the man swallowed.

'Not a pretty sight, hey?' the man asked him, self-conscious but not perturbed.

Peter smiled wanly. He confined himself to Sadie, pouring her a glass of wine and finding somewhere between them to put her purse. Sadie wanted to go to England and was interested in the more practical details, the cost of the flight, the chance of finding work, what was the National Health Service, taking apartments in London, were there any other places in England; Stratford or something, Edinburgh. She had a perfect capacity for totally ignoring the huge blob which was less than two feet away. Peter's answers were vague clichés. He could feel Sadie getting annoyed, and also the fat man sitting as an amused tribunal in between his glasses of water and his strands of lettuce. Not a pretty sight. It was a strange thing to say.

Their food came, and the conversation broke off. Peter asked for more bread and made a series of sandwiches, which he shovelled down with the help of the wine. He noticed the fat man stirring his coffee for about five minutes. He then drank it, one-off, and ordered another cup. There was a pause when Peter had cleared his plate and Sadie was still eating. Peter pushed his chair back; he met the eyes of the fat man. This time there was no getting out of it. The fat man spoke.

'You're English?'

'Yes. And you?'

'American. Or should I say, New Yorker?'

Peter didn't care what he said. 'Is there a difference?'

'There certainly is. New York is something on its own.'

The fat guy might have been a tramp, his suit showed no great signs of any devotion to appearance; threadbare, shiny and several foodstains. And either he had no mirror or else he had a razor that couldn't handle overhangs. Sadie was still eating, her face fixed firmly on the other tables.

'What do you do?' Peter asked.

'I believe that everybody is beautiful.'

Sadie had great self-control, Peter had to fumble around with the water in order to hide the explosion of laughter that pillared up from his belly. The fat man wasn't at all concerned. He said: 'You are a very good-looking young couple.'

'Thank you,' said Peter.

'Are you married?'

'No, we're just friends.'

'And lovers,' Sadie put in, exclusively, without embarrassment for the fat man; blandly asserting her wish for them to be left alone.

'Lovers . . .' the fat man got the message, '. . . well you're very lucky young people.' He finished his coffee and seemed to be about to leave.

'Why don't you have a glass of wine?' Peter asked him.

'That's very kind of you, I thank you. I feel that your girlfriend would like it better if you were alone.'

'We've had a hard day; we got mixed up in a shooting. Sadie? Let's relax a little.' He took her arm, she looked at him quizzically, as much as to say 'Where's it going to get you?' She shook her head, slightly bewildered, and smiled. 'You don't want to drink too much on top of the pills, but I guess another glass won't hurt. I'll just go to the ladies' room.'

She brushed his lips with her own, and took her purse with her, not forgetting to smile ever so wanly at the fat man. Peter poured him a wine.

'We're both a bit exhausted. She's friendly, she didn't mean to be off-putting.'

'Your very good health.' The fat man raised his glass. 'She's right, you know; the city's a dangerous place. Not many people talk to strangers. It isn't a wise thing to do.'

'Yeah, but if you don't do it, you end up talking to yourself and maybe shooting at other people. Why do *you* talk to other people?'

The fat man shrugged. 'I was always ugly. I was very unhappy when I was a child, I didn't have a woman until I paid for one at twenty-eight. I thought then that I'd got nothing to lose and my experience tells me that I was right. I started doing it out of desperation; there are a lot of losers in this town, no point in getting hung up about it. Together you can have some success. Togetherness brings ripeness and its own reward.' The fat man paused to let the words sink in.

It would be difficult to continue. Christ, thought Peter, where's Sadie? He offered another banality in part exchange: 'Action brings good fortune.'

'Truly,' said the fat man, sipping his wine.

'So what do you *do*?' Peter blurted at him.

'I'm a psychotherapist.' The fat man looked across at him, heavy-lidded with credentials.

'Oh no ...' Peter put his head in his hands. Sadie returned and sat down beside him.

'Pardon me?' she asked, by way of an introduction to the conversation.

'I was just telling your boyfriend that I am by trade a psycho-therapist.' The fat man smiled and indicated Peter's posture. Sadie smiled back.

'I think he's a little tired of the medical profession. My name's Sadie, I'm in the same type of work, *physio*therapy.'

'Well, well ...' the fat man beamed, 'my name is Paul, and this is ...?'

'Peter; I'm in the afterbirth side. Mop-therapy.' Peter hauled his chin into the cup of his hand. 'Pleased to meet you.'

'Not for long, surely, the mopping?' The fat man was perplexed. 'You seem to have some intelligence.'

'Not for any longer than I needed to. It was a question of money rather than intellectual involvement. And the cleansing isn't what you might call spiritual.' Both Sadie and the fat man laughed, the fat man said:

'Sanitation doesn't have its own reward?'

'Maybe, but I should imagine that those receiving it spend it pretty quickly on psychotherapists.' Peter thought suddenly of the Polack and what he had said about the intimacy between the sickos and the crushed foetuses. He wondered if Sadie knew about it, he had forgotten to tell her. It was better not to mention it. The fat man and Sadie were still smiling, though the fat man's, Paul's, eyes were more shrewd. He took up the conversation.

'That's what I mean. You should transfer to my business. I remember what you said. Action brings good fortune. That's good, people like to hear it, they like to hear it spelt out. And you're a listener. You could make it.'

'Action brings good fortune?' Sadie considered it. 'Yes, that's good, he's right. It's even rhythmical.'

'Yes, I got it off an old rock and roll album.' Peter laughed. The fat man merely shrugged.

'It's a good slogan, people like to hear that kind of thing. It gives them confidence. Who cares where it comes from? You don't tell them that. You got to see it this way: that painter guy, Warhol, he paints bean cans, people pay a lot of money for them, and what are they? Bean cans. You can't even get any beans out of them and half the world is starving.' Peter laughed; Sadie smiled, a bit distracted.

'Soup,' Peter said, 'he paints soup cans.'

'Soup, beans, who gives a shit ... you think some kid in Africa, even the Bronx, can afford to get choosy? Hell, you sell them democracy; you sell them beans if they're poor and pictures of beans if they're rich. That way you cross-section the world market.'

Peter thought he was marvellous, but he could feel Sadie's openness evaporating.

'You want some more wine, let's drink some more wine ...' the fat man turned to contact the waitress. Sadie shook her head. It was reasonable, the restaurant had nearly emptied, there were only three other tables occupied. Peter held up both hands in the ten-minute suggestion. Sadie nodded, and fixed on the figure by looking at her watch. She glared at him. The fat man eased himself round on the chair to face them again.

'Is that how the psychotherapy business works?' Peter asked, and was delighted with the answer.

'It is. I try to keep people happy, beautiful, sane and in contact with each other. Pain out. That's a chant, like a mantra. Pain out. I suppose that's what your little nurse friend does with the massage?' His eyes twinkled mischievously.

Sadie flinched. 'After a lot of training.'

'You have any training?' Peter asked the fat guy.

'All the training you need. There's no way I don't know about problems. I've been fat and ugly since I was a kid, right on through high school and adolescence I was ugly. I didn't get on a woman until I was thirty, I was so ugly.' His repetition was for Sadie's benefit, just another slight kick at her womb. This time she rose to it.

'You can't be much help to any woman, can you? If you never had any contact with them, or if you think contact with a woman means getting over her.'

The fat man shrugged it off and, in one of the most stunning put-downs Peter had ever seen, he calmly poured her a glass of wine. For a second he was going to get it back in his face, Sadie picked up the glass, her body swayed forward.

'There's a bit of cork in there,' Peter said. He took the glass and her hand up to his face and looked into the wine.

'Do you carry a gun?' Peter asked the fat man. Sadie's hand relaxed.

'I don't need one. My job is to calm people. I find I can usually do this with words, not with guns.'

Sadie looked at her watch, and excused herself to make a phone call about the car.

'Don't you need a licence for what you do?'

'Do you think that the government should control psychotherapy? You're young. Don't you think that's dangerous? I was under the impression that young people were demonstrating against that kind of thing; the government controlling the people.'

'Having a licence wouldn't control the use of guns.'

'That's because it's the gun that's licensed, not the people who hold it. If you were to apply the system to psychotherapy, it would be the therapists who would be restricted, or the ideas. We aim to have an open society in America, that's what the Movement is for. The only reason that people come to me is because they want to, not because I carry a lot of letters after my name, which, in America, anyone can get if they pay for it at college. To have therapists from rich families only, is that what you're driving for?'

'No ... but do you know what you're doing?'

'I don't do anything.' The fat man held his eye.

'Bullshit.'

'I don't do a damn thing, I don't read any books, I don't tell people what to do.'

'Well how do you get any patients?'

'When I started, I put an advertisement in the newspaper.'

Peter was incredulous, he offered his hands up in manifestation of the same. The fat man pinned him down.

'Lemme tell you. This is America. If you got the guts to be a salesman, you can sell anything. There's a whole dumb mass of buyers. One thing this country has got is money; so much of it that people have the feeling that it can't buy anything of value. So you charge a high enough price and people relate to it as being worth something, not the end product but the actual experience of spending money. They walk into Sears and the experience lasts them five minutes; they come to a psychotherapy session and it lasts an hour. And because

I don't give them an object to take home with them, they don't get bored with it, and so they come back.'

'And they don't blow your cover?'

The fat guy poured more wine. 'What cover? I don't kid them. I pay taxes, and you should see the taxes in this city. You may be a genius, I'm no genius. I was ugly and fat and fucked-up. I went to see this guy who had an advertisement in the Village Voice. You pay five bucks for an hour. What's five bucks? Who hasn't got five bucks? It's a democratic figure. The room was full of people; twenty, maybe twenty-five. They all had problems, they wanted to talk about them; they didn't need him. They acknowledged that it was his apartment, he gave them coffee, maybe some pot and a few words as he walked round the room. He'd met a lot of people; he wasn't dumb; his words were objective. He didn't have to get involved in the encounter, he could keep a clear head. Everybody knew that they had problems or they wouldn't be there. So they talked to each other about their problems; they helped each other. You can't do that in the city; you have a telephone and a book of numbers, the music is too loud in the clubs, you feel like an asshole in front of somebody who hasn't got problems.

'So I went there twice and it was doing me a lot of good. I went to bed with a girl the second time. So I ask the guy, what credentials has he got? None. What harm is he doing? None. What is the effect? Good. How much money is he making? A hundred, a hundred and fifty a night. With that kind of money, in two years you can retire, you can afford to go to a therapist with a string of letters, you can fuck the best-looking broads in the city, you're beautiful. This is America. It's a growth industry. And what does your little nurse do? How does she get the car in a private garage? She's beautiful. Who doesn't need a massage? You tell me. She's over by the door, she can't face being beautiful.'

Peter was pulled back into the present. The chairs were all on the tables around them. He and the fat guy stood up. The restaurant's music system was off and the sound of a piano drifted in from somewhere down the street.

The fat guy wanted to pay for their dinner, but Peter refused. Sadie was silent and tired and they still had to drive out to Jersey. They stood on the pavement, waiting for two cabs.

'New York . . .' The fat guy breathed his loneliness up towards the buildings. 'It never sleeps . . .'

A cab arrived from downtown and swung across to the pavement.

'Can we give you a ride?' Sadie asked.

'Thank you, we're going different ways,' the fat guy said. Sadie disappeared into the back of the cab.

'See you, Paul. You take care.' Peter shook the pudgy hand and followed after Sadie. The face looked into the cab.

'You enjoy yourself while you're here.' He closed the cab door and their driver didn't loiter.

'Enough ...' Peter's head collapsed on to Sadie's shoulder. She was waiting.

'That's it,' she shook her head, 'that's New York; let's get home.'

Dawn. The streetlights battled with it to brighten up the day. They collected the car and crossed the city, heading for the Lincoln Tunnel and Route 3. The sanitation trucks attacked the streets, small yellow warning lights winked. Sadie sped past them down 42nd Street towards the river, some classical music low on the radio.

The city passed them in a dreamy sprawl, its shapes softened by the grey light, draped in its litter. It was remarkably beautiful, emptied of its blood, struggling out of its shrouds and free of its sociologists; the gush of water from its hydrants to help it breathe, the few trees limp and shy.

Their route took them part of the same way that Peter had come with Bob, several months before, when Bob had collected him from the airport. Now, way up, he could see the stack of planes, already glittering in the sunlight that hadn't yet hit ground level. Peter realized how little he had done, but at least he was still there. Still where? One more night with Sadie; in fact, this night *was* the one more night. Then it would be Bob's apartment. Why? For lack of anything better. Not good enough. And it was dawn. There was no sense to anything. He looked out of the window.

'How much is a plane ticket to California?' he asked Sadie, later.

'It's expensive,' she kept her eyes on the road, 'you'd do better to look for a ride.'

'Yeah.'

He might just as well stand on the side of the Expressway and see what happened.

Sadie broke the silence.

'I feel closer to you now than I did.' She took one hand off the wheel and turned down the radio, waiting for him to say something.

They arrived at the Turnpike toll-booth and she wound down her window to drop a quarter into the basket. It was six lanes. To the left of them a family, with children sleeping; and three lanes to the right a shaded man in a light-blue Mustang looked Sadie over and revved his engine before accelerating away in excessive style. Sadie was nervous. They cruised at forty in a central lane.

Peter put a finger out and changed stations on the radio. Jazz/rock music. Someone was alive somewhere. It was the end of a track. A familiar voice introduced the next number and gave a weather outlook. The music started again. 'Under the Boardwalk.'

'Wasn't that . . . ?' Peter wondered.

'Yes, it's the same guy. Carol's date. He has an early morning show.'

'He hardly said anything.'

'He never does. Except when he's with people. When he's broadcasting to the East Coast, he's baby blue.'

'Would it be all right if I left a suitcase at your apartment?'

Sadie nodded slowly. 'Will you be coming back for it, or shall I send it on?'

'If I don't come back for it, you can keep it,' Peter joked.

'Thanks, thanks for the thought.' She fumbled to get out a cigarette.

'Sadie . . . Sadie . . .' he gave her a light, 'what do you expect me to say?'

'If you can't think for yourself; nothing. Just nothing at all. When are you going?'

'As soon as possible, maybe this afternoon.'

'Don't be dumb, you've had no sleep. Anyway, it's Sunday; there's no traffic. Do you know where to go from?'

It was better that they discuss arrangements.

'No.'

'Fantastic. Are you packed up?'

'No.'

'I'll drop you off on the Turnpike tomorrow morning.'

'You don't have to.'

'I'd like to.'

He kissed her.

'I'm driving,' she said. 'And it's nearly our exit. Don't make me screw it up; otherwise we'll be stuck on this road for ever.'

There was a flash of red and a lot of horn and the back of a coupé cutting them up, then accelerating away from them up the exit road.

'Crazy bastard . . .' Peter threw after it.

'It's Carol, she went dancing in the city.' Sadie laughed.

'What are you doing?' Peter demanded, as she stamped her foot down for the chase.

'Come on, live a little. We'll beat her home.'

'You won't. Not against *that* car.'

'Wanna bet?'

They arrived just after her; Sadie knew the back roads but still had Peter scared at her cornering. She was into the chase and furious at losing it. She slammed her door shut with all the gaiety she could contrive, and skipped across to open Carol's door for her, swinging her purse round and round in the air. She fell into Carol's arms and they hi'd and laughed and walked into the building, Sadie slipping an arm round Peter along the way and roping him into their bubble. They hi'd and chorused to a bewildered and sleepy George, and kept themselves laughing into the elevator. Then it lulled over the buttons, and Peter put in:

'We heard your boyfriend on the radio.'

'We don't talk about men on Sundays.' Sadie tensed.

'And the radio is the best place for him.' Carol affirmed. She was pale and sleepless.

'We'll stay up and we'll eat lunch early and we won't be morbid, we'll open the champagne.' Sadie led them at a brisk pace down the corridor. Carol looked at her warily.

'Is she all right?' she asked Peter as they trailed behind.

'We had a strange day and night.' Peter didn't want to do any confiding; he was too tired.

'Are you going?' she guessed.

'Tomorrow.'

'Oh . . .' Carol took a deep breath.

'It's not that serious, is it?' Peter looked at her.

'No . . .' she laughed, '. . . let's go in and get stoned. I've got the first reservation on the shower.'

They all showered, one by one, and changed their clothes to sit around over whatever was in the freezer, the champagne combining deliriously with their exhaustion. They joked about the city and work, they danced ludicrously and fell about, the three of them, into the afternoon, nothing mattered. Carol gave them a fashion show, they got Peter up in thousand-dollar drag, Carol slipped towards and away from nakedness, Peter wondered what was wrong with Bob, he wanted Sadie, they danced, Sadie was near him, quietly, kissing him and handing him the last of the champagne, the joint was strong, or something was strong, she led him to her bed, it's all over now. He was out.

They watched him sleeping.

'Fuck it . . .' Sadie moaned. Carol took her in her arms and they cried together, standing up.

Peter didn't see it. He was out. He had a long, dreamless sleep; right through the late afternoon, the evening, the night. It was just daylight again when Sadie was shaking him gently awake. He had never felt so refreshed. He wondered where the party was, until she told him the time and he saw that she was in her nurse's uniform.

'Sadie?'

'Let's move. I have to be at work in two hours. We've got a long way to drive. Carol sends her love and says happy travels.'

'Where am I going?'

'West.'

'All my stuff is at Bob's.'

'It's here. Bob and I packed it up. You just have to decide what to take. And give Bob a call. Now hurry. And don't make it difficult, please.'

He heard the sound of the coffee machine. Some clean clothes were laid out. He shook himself and dressed. He had an extraordinarily clear head. And no map. He went through his bags quickly, deciding to take only the one, and the bare minimum of clothes, and the bottle of Laird's which was there from Bob. Sadie would look after the rest.

He put his arm round her in the kitchen, and hugged her silently. He ate the enormous breakfast that she had cooked. She was very, very tired. Her eyes were red.

'I haven't got a map.'

'You don't need a map. And there's three hundred dollars. Bob will wire the rest, care of American Express. There's an office in every city.'

They had another cup of coffee, looking at each other without expression. Sadie laid her hand over his arm.

'Call Bob. He's not sleeping.'

Peter went through to the lounge and sat in a chair near the phone; he dialled slowly. The phone buzzed four or five times and Bob answered.

'Yup.'

'Thanks for packing everything up.'

'No problem. Send me a postcard from Kansas City; yeah, that sounds an interesting place.'

'It might be.'

'Sure. Well, I'll be seein' you. I'm going back to bed.'

'Yes. Thanks, Bob.'

'No sweat. Don't get your head busted.'

The phone went dead. Peter put the receiver back. No point in being morbid. Sadie had the keys to the first ride.

Marina Warner

After Veronese's 'Susannah and the Elders'

'In Babylon there lived a man named Joachim. He had married Susannah ... a woman of great beauty ... At midday when everyone had gone, Susannah used to take a walk in her husband's garden. The two elders, who used to watch her every day as she came in to take her walk, gradually began to desire her ...'

Daniel 13, 1–8 (Jerusalem Bible)

MARINA WARNER was born in 1946, and went to school in Egypt, Belgium and Berkshire. She read French and Italian at Lady Margaret Hall, Oxford, where she edited *Isis*, the university magazine. She has worked as a feature writer and critic for magazines and newspapers, and reviews regularly for the *Sunday Times*. Her books include two historical studies in female symbolism: *Alone of All Her Sex, The Myth and the Cult of the Virgin Mary* (1976) and *Joan of Arc, The Image of Female Heroism* (Penguin, 1983), and two novels: *In a Dark Wood* (1977) and *The Skating Party* (1982). She has also written stories for children, including *The Wobbly Tooth*, to be published in 1984.

The night was full of noises, the chatter of birds and the whir and zing of insects. With your eyes shut you felt the trees closing in on the house, pressing up against the roof eaves and the verandah balustrade, their boughs astir. But your eyelids parting in the first pale humid light, you saw again how sparsely the trees grow and far between, and could not distinguish the bright woodpecker or the chafing insects that seemed so near. When you pulled yourself from your bed to look out more carefully, the dew on the lawn glittered. Kells were hung from springing blade to blade like crystal hammocks. You knew it was going to be hot, as hot as it could be in that enclave of gardens and suburban houses cordoned off from the boom city on the peninsula.

You: I. *I* knew it was going to be hot. I stepped slowly, the heat already flattening the breath in my body, my footsteps on the boards of my bedroom Man Friday prints of dark sweat on the sheen. I often call myself you, as you do. I think of myself as 'you', as I go about things from day to day. Susannah, what a fool you are to eat one more piece of bread for breakfast in the morning than you resolved. You'll never lose weight if you carry on like that. I think it's seeing myself through others' eyes (your eyes) makes the vocative more comfortable than the nominative. I was happy for my first person singular to be you, until – but you shall hear.

Joachim had left for town when I got up; he rises early so that he can return at lunchtime and lie down during the dog heat of the day. The towel in the bathroom was still wet from his shower. Nothing dries here. I took another towel from the store; the jet refreshed me. I wished the school term had not begun again, as I drank my coffee and refused the bread the amah offered me, the light, wholesome bread that represents the best legacy of the European power that colonized this country. With the children still on holiday, I could put off doing the firm's accounts; we could drive to the windward side of the peninsula

and sit together in the lapping air and guess as each wave swelled,
Would it make the beach and spill itself there? Dan would pick one
breaker; Seth another, their mother a third, but absently, often
forgetting to follow her chosen contender with her gaze, stolen from the
ocean by the straight smooth limbs of her sons, who printed upon her
own features the special laughter of loving and of peace that comes with
the contemplation of youth when it knows nothing of its own power
and loveliness. Oh, that was *yours*, Seth would say with disgust, as his
mother's choice unfurled its scalloped banner before them. Was it,
darling? I don't think so. 'And you're not even playing properly,' Dan,
furious, remonstrated at his mother's try at diplomatic defeat. 'It was
yours. You're pretending it wasn't so Seth can win.' More disgust,
bodies looped together on the sand; separating, down by the water
again. 'Look a crab! It'll get you.' They ran past ablaze in the light
that was shaken off the sea's thousand facets, they were oblivious,
plural in their doubled presence, but singular, invincibly singular in
their regard on the world that looked back at them and in which they
moved.

I remember the end for me of that Edenic stage when shame had no
place and I never looked upon myself to see myself with the eyes of
others. I was eight: Seth will be eight next year, Dan is one year
younger. My mother brought the coat of a guest to her bedroom, and
caught me red-handed, out of bed and making up in her mirror. I was
transfixed by the perfect lopped cylinder of her lipstick, as if her mouth
had sliced the tip sideways like a salami. I was trying right up against
the glass to stiffen my lips into a shape that would fit the smooth end,
but the breath misted the mirror, my hand slipped, and smeared like an
infant who's gorged at the jampot, I was discovered. My heart beat
with fear, but my mother laughed. She wiped off the scarlet mess and
told me, as my punishment for getting out of bed and being so vain, I
must come downstairs. There, I was to recite to her friends the poem
I'd told her I'd learned by heart.

I didn't want to. The faces of her friends, cigarettes and hairstyles,
corrugated eye pouches, thread veins and pungent fragrances of hair
lotion, women's perfume, assailed me. I backed up against the books
on the shelves and stared up past their attending phalanx to look at the
words printed in my head:

'I will let loose against you the fleet-footed vines,
I will call in the Jungle to stamp out your lines,
The walls shall fade before it,

The house-beams shall fall,
And the Karela, the bitter Karela
Shall cover you all.'

Mowgli had watched the people whose settlements marched with the jungle and encroached; they had not spied on him, let alone watched him. But I was watched.

I concentrated on the spool of spinning print in my mind's eye; but I still saw them as they watched me and though I found it uncomfortable, even excruciating to be the focus of their eyes, I wanted terribly to please, to please them and to please my mother. When I ended and they clapped and clucked and cooed and exclaimed, 'Frances, darling, what a memory your little girl's got!' I detected a note of respect, but not pleasure. They were impressed by the child reciting, mouth a round O of enmity like a perverted chorister, but they did not warm to me. ('You're nothing but a big fat idiot, Susannah, you choose a poem like that and then you want people to like it and to love you . . . What do you expect?')

In the kitchen now, the amahs were quarrelling, they are always yapping at each other, baring gold teeth and smoothing their hair over brow and skull, wretchedly working back and forth like hired mourners. Usually I try and part them by assigning them to different tasks or, in my pidgin, try and discover the cause of their falling out and bring about a reconciliation; but today, with the heat stacked on the lip of the coming day like a storm cloud on the horizon, I couldn't bear the shrill and squealing misery of their strife. I called out. They came, gesturing their mutual antipathy and murmuring imprecations. I told them to take the day off. 'Holidays,' I said. They did not look altogether pleased; to be relieved of a day's work robbed them of the intense pleasure of recriminating all day together.

But I wanted silence – and solitude.

The women left. I tilted the slats so that light fell on to the table where I do Joachim's accounts; I sat down to the work without relish. We have to keep the books so scrupulously, else the new government will use slipshod accountancy as a pretext to take over assets of foreign companies like ours. The columns must show materials we have imported, materials we have bought locally, wages we have paid. I have to enter the same sets of figures four or five times: in the records of the individual contract or building, in the different tax books, direct and indirect, in the client's book, in the company's book for the client's records, and for our company's annual accounts. It's the kind of work I wish I wasn't good at; the struggle I have between doing it nimbly and finding it so dull wears me out.

The sweat stood out on my forehead and rolled into my eyes. I wiped it back into my hair. I made notes on the items that exceeded Joachim's estimate for the new hotel on the Leeward side. I flapped my blouse to inflate it, and felt soothed as it slowly emptied and settled again, cooling me a touch. I made a separate set of calculations, working out how the excess on the tiles round the hotel pool could be lost on other items. (They'd come from Italy, 20 per cent over budget.) It's too hot to work, Susannah, it's too hot.

I lifted a slat between my fingers. Light was moving on the grass without glints: the dew dry already.

You could lie under the flame tree, in the shade, Susannah, with a book. There's no one here. You'll be screened by the fence. I dropped the blind, turned back to the ledgers. Enough for one morning.

I peeled off my blouse and stepped under the shower again, rinsing the salt of my sweat out of my hair, holding the jet to sluice the stickiness from pit and crutch, as my mother said when I was young.

The rattan mat unrolled under the scarlet spires of the broad-leaved tree was fresh to the contact of my skin; I stripped off my clean blouse and skirt and lay back in the dapple. But the film of warmth that clung to all forms clothed me the next instant, enfolding anything that interrupted the soft density of space, my body too alongside all the other shapes that lifted and moved the soft heavy air, the humming insects, the disclosed blooms, the birds that flopped rather than darted in amongst the leaves.

Joachim had made love to me as soon as the guests of the night before had gone; he had needed no encouragement from me. They had excited him, and I'd accepted his greedy taking of me for himself, although his desire, mediated through theirs, was ugly. It wasn't the first time that Joachim had said, before some business associates arrived to eat with us, 'Put on something, well, you know, something ...' and then described curves in the air, the contours of imagined breasts and hips. We ate in the garden, with the mosquito candles smoking. There were two guests. One, the representative from the Belgian property company that has won the concession for the new racecourse (as if the colony's needs weren't met by the old course in the hills), was a handsome man of a florid, fleshy sort, with grey curls swept back and wet on the nape of his sunburnt neck. Dierek laughed easily, with a loud, urgent wholeheartedness that at first I found pleasant. The second man, an Italian, was the architect, Saldieri, and I'd seen his award-winning design for the grandstand in the local press. It was graceful and ingenious. He's adapted the traditional construction with bamboo timber and bamboo leaf thongs to enamelled steel in the European High Tech style. It made it easier for me at first to talk to him than to his employer's representative, but later things turned out differently. Saldieri was a reticent man with a brooding forehead and dark eyes, that for all their size and depth of colour were oddly empty at contact. He made little dents in the tablecloth with his nails as he strummed.

Joachim wanted the site contract even more than he'd wanted to build the new hotel, and I was to help him. 'Susannah, I have to build so much shit. These plans are beautiful. I'd never look back – *we'd* never look back if I built that grandstand. And I can do it. The work force has never been better; the foreman's got them eating out of his hand. It will be perfect. Saldieri himself will be amazed at the quality of the work out here. You must help me to persuade them. You must.'

Before they came last night, he looked me over and twitched his lips with appreciation. 'You are beautiful, Susannah,' he said.

I'm proud of Joachim. He's an adventurer, but without the adventurism. He came out here on an inspiration when he could have stayed riskless at home, and he learned the language and the byways of the country's customs with speed and energy until the natural suspicion and xenophobia of a once-colonized zone evaporated and government and commerce liked to deal with him. But I flinched at the way he looked at me as he considered the effect I would have on the resistance of Dierek and Saldieri. I flinched first and then I warmed. Joachim's eyes aren't empty, but mischievous, and the sex mischief in them when he looked me over buzzed inside me till I giggled.

The evening had continued like that; when my butterfly sleeve dropped off my shoulder as I poured Saldieri some mineral water he wanted, I let it fall and even stretched my neck to set off the bareness of my shoulder. Saldieri watched, but said nothing. Dierek did: to Joachim, he said, 'Your wife is a splendid woman, Joachim.' And then, exploding with laughter, 'Thank God for Caucasian women, eh, Paolo! The little girls downtown ...' and he pulled his bright eyes until they slitted, '... are fine for an hour, but ... Yes, you're a lucky devil, Joachim. She's splendid.'

I was glad when it was over, when Joachim undressed me brusquely and sank into me with as much necessity as if he'd been caressing me for hours.

I turned on the rattan, and tried to pitch myself back from slumber into the day. Something soft touched my cheek. A daytime moth. I put my hand up to brush her away, gently, and a hand closed round mine and a voice said, 'Hello, Susannah. Hello there.'

I tried to cover myself with one arm and held out the other hand to Saldieri, who stood there as serious as the night before, to take my shirt back from him. I think it was a plea too, that gesture. He held it out to me, but did not let go. I jumped up and pulled the rattan with me, like a shield; Dierek stepped behind me and laughed.

'Joachim,' I cried, 'Joachim is coming back.'

Dierek spluttered on his guffaw. 'He's meeting us here,' he said. 'He had invited us to lunch, didn't he tell you?'

Saldieri let go my hand and cupped my face. 'In half an hour, Susannah.' He intoned my name. 'Lots can happen in half an hour.' And he took his hand from my face and lifted the rattan like a curtain and looked me up and down.

You're a splendid woman, Susannah, they want to feast on you because you're beautiful. Aren't you proud of being beautiful? Show them, Susannah, let them in, your husband will be pleased and proud that his friends understand how fortunate he is, won't he?

Think, how flattering, your beauty overpowers them. You're not moved, and they are weak with wanting you. What's there to fear? Dance for them, Susannah, show them a leg and more, they'll clutch at you and fall on all fours for a touch, you could make them eat out of the palm of your hand.

Cry dirty bastard, tighten your contempt till it matches their look and breaks them, hurt them with your coldness, hit out where they mind. Call them no good rapists, where are your balls? Call that a cock?

But remember your mother, yes. I wish you'd learn to be more gracious. Yes. There's nothing in the world as unattractive as foul language in a woman. Yes. Do try and be more feminine darling. Yes. That's better. Yes. Good, darling.

And pity. Don't forget pity. Men need our pity.

In a tropical house, every room gives on to every other without locks, nothing but flimsy partitions. I ran, I began dressing myself; Dierek slid the door and watched. Saldieri passed behind him and came in; I had trousers on, the first tee shirt I could find.

'Please,' said Saldieri. He held me and began to move against me with scissor-like sawing of his legs. 'Please, Susannah,' he said again.

Dierek was crouched against the wall and holding himself, and Susannah, you were not there, not in your skin your bones your flesh, child, no, but in the corner of the ceiling, microscopic and insect-like on the plaster. You watched yourself. Then Dierek groaned and then his groaning turned to crowing and you Susannah you were watching the little girl performing for the grown-ups. Try and recall it Susannah, what was it, mixed up with your longing that they love you and find you wonderful, what was it? Yes, Susannah, remember, the song against people. And the insect flew down from the ceiling and into your eye, your eye.

How long have you been watching me? How long has my body been inside your eyes? How long has my ordinary flesh, my secret part, been yours, how long has your spying on me turned me inside out?

I know how perilous the inside of things can be: I know the blue smoothness of the fish when the fishwife guts it for me in the market; the mandorla of evisceration on the anatomical plate, fruit and flowers of flesh of the inside made into an outside emblem; the red-black juice of overripe tomatoes squashed under careless shoppers' feet; the dentist's intimate medicine-scented finger in my gums and on the silvery underface of my rose-veined cheek; I know the soft crumbly pollution inside gloves. My sons' illnesses turn the inside out, and only the most loved and closest can bear it, the inner body . . . bodied forth.

You Susannah are being rendered down; your fat and juices are simmering in the round hot cauldron of their wilful eyes. Yes. They are reducing you, Susannah, you are leaking out of your openings and fissures, you are in their gaze, holes and nooks and crannies, nipple a nozzle and mouth a drain, and even your navel opening, and no, no, no, no, the pulpy shell of your vulva is widening widening in their many-tongued look until there's going to be nothing left of you but a round O, Susannah. Let me disappear. Make this dissolution of my self complete until nothing is left of me but my print on the floor. Let me drain away through the good earth where the insects tick and the plumed creatures peck. You have made me nothing by your watching. Let me be nothing.

No! And I swung at the trembling body of the man clamped around my legs and dabbling in the ichor of my flesh.

'Get out of here,' I shouted, 'Get out.' Then I pulled Saldieri up from where he lay shuddering and pushed him towards the door and shouted to Dierek. He went, wiping himself, and gave me a finger. 'You whore,' he said.

They met Joachim in the garden; he flung an arm around Saldieri and led him back into the house. He was apologizing for keeping them waiting. He hadn't realized the appointment was so early. Had they had a drink at least?

Dierek shrugged. 'Susannah was occupied with something else,' I heard him say.

Saldieri coughed in his dry throat. 'She had a visitor.'

Joachim my husband looked bewildered. His arm fell from round the men's necks. 'Susannah,' he cried, 'Susannah?'

I waited for him to reach me. 'Tell them to wait,' I said to my husband, and we went indoors together.

'Joachim,' I was speaking quietly under my breath. 'They came early, I was in the garden . . .' I choked, I gestured at my body.

Joachim looked at me. 'What are you saying, Susannah . . . ?' His face went white; two spots of colour flamed on his cheeks, on his forehead the sweat stood out, and he buried his head in my shoulder and groaned, 'Are you all right?'

'What are you saying, Ingeniere?' said Saldieri, when Joachim went out to the two men and asked them to leave. 'She is lying to you, you poor fool . . .' And he made the sign of the two-horned beast.

Joachim's eyes wavered back to me, standing on the verandah.

I came down the steps, slowly. I was shaking. 'Joachim,' I said, 'believe me.'

Joachim looked at me, 'Of course.'

Dierek guffawed.

'Stronzo,' said Saldieri. 'Povero stronzo.'

Dierek said, 'She was in the garden.' And he swivelled his hips lasciviously. 'With a local boy. He jumped over the hedge when he saw us . . . Ask her, see if she can deny it . . .'

Saldieri: 'Yes, he jumped over the wall when he saw us.'

Joachim: 'The hedge? Where? The wall? Where?'

Saldieri's eyes flew round the garden. 'Out of the gate, I mean.'

'But I was driving in . . .' said Joachim.

'Go,' I said, 'go away, you should have more shame.'

I took Joachim by the arm and led him to the house.

Joachim never believed Dierek and Saldieri; sometimes I find him beside me in bed, teeth clenched, with tears of rage standing in his sleepless eyes. 'My wife, they tried to rape my wife . . .' I hold him and try and smooth away the knots and tangles in his spirit.

But once he warned me, 'Susannah, don't ever take your clothes off, even when you are alone.'

So I am to blame in part; also, I know that the sight of the grandstand's rising scaffolding fills him with rancour. But he keeps back his disappointment, out of respect.

*

I was walking in the old quarter the other day and I got lost. The stepped alleys defy a European's bump of locality, and it's easy to stray. I turned a corner of the street near the vegetable market that I thought was familiar, and I found myself in the courtyard of what must have been once a grand establishment, now converted into tenements. The temple in the corner was guarded by lion dogs, washing strung from jaw to jaw. The children who always surround a 'round-eye' if you stray jumped around me, some shouting 'Hey! baby' and 'Cute! Cute!', even 'Cuteypie' – the last phrases remembered from the war. I tried to cry above their hubbub for directions back to the market centre, and they swept me on and into a chamber which was curtained off from the yard. An old lady was sitting there in the semi-darkness, in silence. She pointed out the way, and I thanked her, and turned to go. As I turned, a figure moved behind one of the columns of the building. The child had crept out of cover to take me in. But she? he? did not move fast enough, and when I saw the child I cried out.

Sometimes in the East you still see lepers, begging at the entrances of large gathering places. No doubt one or two will sit patiently at the gates of the new racecourse, and beg their bread from us as we enter. I don't know what had deformed the child who stayed within, beside the silent matriarch in her dark room. She – I do think of the child as a girl – stopped my heart with horror, and upon the instant with pity too; but if she had not ducked away from my sight but grabbed at me like all the other children of that place, I do not think I could have put out my hand to take hers or held her disfigured and swollen countenance without shrinking. As it was, with my coward's shriek, I fell away for a moment from humankind, when I caught a glimpse of a child who had learned to keep away from being watched.

Paul Winstanley

Pterodactyl

PAUL WINSTANLEY has published a number of short stories over the last twenty years, most recently in *Ambit*. He lives in County Durham.

The sea was quiet and cold. Ripples from the ebbing tide lagged behind to run in tiredly among the stones beneath Crick's borrowed wellingtons. He sat on a tilting slab of rock, hunched over, with MacAlistair's huge binoculars dangling between his knees, the strap cutting into the back of his neck. The sun had gone in altogether now, and he held himself stiffly to keep from shivering.

Sitting like this, perfectly still, what he was mainly doing was indulging in the discomfort, the cold; in his despondency. His flair was for fiasco: he'd done it again. Herring gulls, herring gulls; one oyster-catcher, one common tern. Not of course the dwindling little tern, no chance; not even the arctic, not the black, nor the roseate. Just to see a bird that he could put that name to. Roseate tern.

The sea no longer came to where he sat, and the stones at his feet had dried to an infinite variety of shades ranging from dull grey to dull green. Low tide would uncover a strip of sand and bring on the wading birds, but if he waited for that he'd petrify. He'd come down at the wrong time. But he had to escape the house.

'Oh, it'd make a change, you're right there,' he'd said to MacAlistair: dubious about it, making him sell his kindness like a used car. Borrow his cottage? – in the northeast of Scotland, in April, by himself? He'd said he felt like getting away for a few days, but . . .

But (he thought unpleasantly now) he didn't need MacAlistair's benevolence, and he for sure didn't need his godforsaken cottage. Or his birdforsaken beach, either. Absurdly, it had been the mention of the birds, the cove, the binoculars, that finally got to his imagination. Birds, now . . . and sea birds above all! – Some unfinished business of his boyhood, a child's enthusiasm: but why not? What had he got that was better?

Unfortunately, those supremely beautiful beings that floated against the sky, hung on translucent wings bright as the sun, then slid aside in one unflickering plunge to the wave crests (revealing in that skimmed second the forked tail silhouette or the wing bar that identified a rarity, oh definitely, I'm positive) – they'd gone. Gone to be other earnest small boys' apparitions, leaving to × 10 magnification and the probity of the latest reference books nothing but herring gulls. And to Crick another sour trudge back to MacAlistair's damp lonely cottage.

He started to get up, the stones grating under his feet so that he was unsure whether he really heard a thin piping note from somewhere. Straightening, he cocked his head to get the direction – and laughed disbelievingly as the veering breeze tossed him a reedy shred of music. At the same time round the point of the cove came a girl about eight years old. She was treading along the water's edge, watching the small waves come in, hopping neatly out of reach whenever one threatened to wet her plimsolled feet. Now and then she held to her ear a little radio which bleated across the distance to Crick with agoraphobic plaintiveness.

He watched her much as he would have watched an avocet or a phalarope. She wore a thin pale blue dress and a white cardigan; her mouse-coloured hair was done in two skimpy plaits secured with rubber bands.

She was coming nearer all the time, and he grew apprehensive at the thought that he might frighten her. In her absorption there was something very private; her mere unawareness of him placed him somehow in the wrong. He couldn't call out – a strange man suddenly shouting at her – and if he waited till she was close enough for a speaking voice he'd probably give her a worse fright.

Then all at once she looked up and saw him, stopped, a wave darted in, almost caught her, she skipped up on to a boulder and laughed: and he laughed with her.

'Hello,' Crick said.

'Hello,' she said. 'I didn't know you were here.'

'*I* thought *I* was the only one.'

'Oh. Could I look through your telescopes?'

'Binoculars.' Crick unslung them from his neck. 'What would you like to look at?'

'Anything. I don't mind.' Odd, he thought, the Brum accent here. She switched off the radio and put it in a pocket of her cardigan.

'How about that seagull over there?' He adjusted the eyepieces and held the binoculars for her. 'See him? Now, is he nice and clear or a bit sort of blurry?' He showed her how to focus, until finally she said, 'Oh, yes! Isn't he *near*? I can see his eyes. Why is he so fierce? He's got a red bit on his beak – is that something's blood? A fish's?'

'No,' Crick said, 'that's for when he's feeding his babies.'

'Has he got babies?'

'Not quite yet, but in a few weeks he may have. They're starting to lay eggs around now. Actually he may be a he or a she – I can't tell. Aren't you awfully cold like that?'

'No.'

She looked at the gull for a while, then lowered the binoculars. 'I don't see about the red bit. How is it for when he's feeding his babies?'

'Well – you see, he brings the food he's caught for them back to the nest sort of half swallowed. Then when he lands at the nest the babies peck at that red spot, and that makes him bring it back up and they eat it.'

'Urgh!' She giggled. 'Is it true?'

'Oh yes, quite true,' said Crick, smiling. 'They don't mind.'

She thought about it. 'But how do they know to peck at the red bit? And why does that make him sick up the food? – yuk!'

'You ask difficult questions. I can't really tell you why. They just know, and he just does. Birds have –'

'Katherine!' – a voice called sharply. '*Kath*'rine!' A woman was standing at the end of the cove.

'Oh,' she said, 'that's my mum.' She got up and hurried towards her on the slippery stones. Some yards off she turned, walking backwards a few steps. 'Thank you,' she said, and smiled.

Her mother waited, staring hard at Crick. He gave a vague wave with the binoculars, an explanation which she left unacknowledged. She had on a white raincoat over red trousers and high-heeled boots. When the child was almost to her she came forward to snatch her hand and led her out of sight, bending over her scoldingly.

The next day, at the end of a couple of hours at the cove, he scrapped the pretence that he cared all that much what species of seabird might drift into focus. He would much rather tell her all about, say, the homely black-headed gull and its seasonal change of face, or the guillemot's pear-shaped egg, than score up the distinguishing marks of a sooty shearwater or a little auk. When, at low tide, a troupe of sanderling scurried along the water's edge with their air of not having a second to lose, he could only watch the end of the beach, hoping she might arrive in time. A pair of razorbills torpedoed by just off the water, so nicely synchronized that he took them at first for one bird and its shadow. Unshared, his pleasure seemed trivial and affected.

That evening he backed his Saab out of MacAlistair's out-house and drove the three miles to the village. The landlord in the little warm pub was civilly inquisitive, and Crick told him he was returning to London tomorrow. But in the morning the sun shone dazzlingly into the red-flagstoned kitchen and by the time he'd breakfasted he'd decided to give it another day.

He left it till the afternoon to go to the cove, and he hadn't been there ten minutes when she arrived. With her was a boy perhaps two years older. Both had on polo-necked sweaters with a matching pattern. A brother. They walked very slowly; now and then she paused to pick up a pebble or a shell, but they seemed hardly to talk. She never looked to see if Crick was there, but somehow they came directly to where he sat.

'Hello,' she said.

'Hello.' Crick felt his smile somehow disproportionate; she wouldn't know why he should be so pleased to see them.

The boy considered him. He held his head turned aside a little, so as to look from the corners of his eyes, a precocious mannerism. Abruptly, he said, 'Let's see that.'

'These?' said Crick, startled. 'Yes, sure you can.' He took the binoculars from round his neck. 'And what's your name?'

'It's Grant,' the girl told him.

'Shall I show you how to use them, Grant?'

'I know how.'

He focused them familiarly, and began to scan the horizon of the sea. Crick saw that he was hiding the effort it cost him to hold them up level, and stopped himself saying mind you don't drop them. Having raked the skyline slowly from one end to the other, twice, the boy began to peer at the top of the cliff. Crick could see nothing there.

'Maybe we can spot some seagulls. Or something else interesting,' he said; and added, 'I think it's time Katherine had a go.'

The boy continued to stare at the clifftop. Eventually he lowered the binoculars and looked at Crick.

'Our caravan's got a television. As a matter of fact it's not a caravan, it's a motor home. You drive it. It has a toilet and a cooker. And a refrigerator. It's the most expensive sort you can get.'

Feeling it was expected, Crick asked, 'Does it really have a television?'

'Yes it does. My dad's an electrician. He can make three hundred and sixty pounds a week if he wants.'

'Well, well. So what are you doing in these parts?'

'We're staying on our auntie's farm,' Katherine said quickly. 'It's lovely.' Her voice seemed to have grown timid.

'It must be. Grant, give the binoculars to Katherine, will you? Yes, television's fine, but I bet you you can find all sorts of things just along this little bit of beach that are even better.' He could hear his voice, sounding all wrong, and he slid a wistful glance at Katherine. Her eyes were lowered, and her hands folded in her lap.

Her brother, looking sullen, was pretending to disentangle the thin strap from his polo-neck. He looked away down the beach. Suddenly he exclaimed, 'What's that?' and put the binoculars to his eyes again.

'Oh, come on! Katherine hasn't had a go all this time.' But the boy was gazing alertly at a point not fifty yards off, among the stones. 'Give them to me!' Crick said in exasperation.

Without taking his eyes from the spot the boy took the binoculars off and handed them to him. Crick looked at him curiously, and focused them in the same direction. Stones. 'There's nothing there at all,' he said, but the boy was still holding his intent posture, and he continued to search – 'So there is! Well.'

He felt kindly towards this loutish child, after all. 'I can tell you what he is: he's a ringed plover.' He held the binoculars for Katherine, trying to aim them at the right place, though without them he'd immediately lost the little bird.

'He's very hard to see, because his colour scheme is so clever. You see, he has a black and white head, very bold markings – have you got him?' – she nodded eagerly '– but they muddle up the outline, so that if your eye happens to look at it it doesn't see *what* it is it's looking at; it doesn't recognize the usual bird's head shape that it knows . . . Then, the rest of him is quite soft brown and white, so that your eye is inclined to take it separately and just see a shape like an ordinary big pebble. Which means that on a beach like this it most likely doesn't notice him at all. You see how he's keeping absolutely still now: do you know why, Grant? Because he's seen us but he knows he's so well camouflaged his best bet is to stay right where he is, and hope we won't see *him*.'

Crick himself had still lost sight of the plover. He was happy, though. 'Forgot I knew all this! I wonder if he's nesting. If he's got – no, stay still, Grant –'

The boy was scrambling to his feet, and now he was running across the stones towards the bird, stumbling and lurching. Crick leaped up and ran after him, furious. The boy had a stone in his fist, and as Crick came up with him he flung it at the plover, which at that instant broke out of its immobility and scuttled away.

One wing was trailing brokenly. 'Got it!' the boy crowed, 'I hit the bugger!' And Crick, even in his horror and rage, grinned as he ran, and at the same time wanted urgently to reassure the child who looked on –

tell her what was really happening, that her brother was falling for an immemorial piece of trickery. The bird fluttered and swerved among the stones with a pathetic show of distress which disguised its nimbleness, keeping just out of reach, drawing its attacker away from a nest which now he could never find. His hand descending Crick thought momentarily of letting the bird finish the lesson, but his indignation was too much – and then he'd missed and overshot the boy, who had tripped and gone headlong on to the stones.

The plover sprang into the air and wheeled away, and Crick swung round to find Katherine, calling, 'It's all right! He wasn't hurt, he was just shamming, see!'

She was still sitting there holding the binoculars in her lap, and he loped back towards her filled with the plover's triumph. He went down on one knee and held her thin little shoulders, and she looked up doubtfully into his face. He could hear the boy approaching, and he said: 'Your brother's just been taught a lesson, hasn't he?'

The boy stood beside them, and waited till Crick turned to him. Blood ran thinly from his nose and down his chin, and again he surveyed Crick in his sidelong pose, a speculative malice where Crick expected tears. He held out a hand to show a deep cut in the palm oozing through embedded grit, and then with one finger lifted his split upper lip to display a broken tooth. 'You did it,' he said, and nodded a kind of promise.

He brought Crick's departing anger back in his throat. 'I'm glad to see it. I think you've got what you had coming to you. I'm only sorry Katherine should have a brother like you.'

The boy spoke expressionlessly to his sister: 'You saw him push me.' Then he turned away and walked off down the beach. With the barest hesitation she got up and followed behind him. She didn't look at Crick.

He sat down and watched them go. The sunshine had become a hard glint off the sea, which rolled and unrolled its edge on the sand lower down the beach.

I can't handle it, he thought after a while; and repeated aloud, 'I just can't handle it.' His sense of outrage needed to appeal to someone, needed confirmation. The children had reached the point and vanished. As soon as he could no longer see them they and what had happened ceased somehow to be factual – or else, like some shocking dream, insisted that they were, while his sense of reality struggled to reject them.

Going over it, he disbelieved himself already. Just like that, for no reason? It only shocks you because you were fantasizing, romanticizing them. Lecturing. You're pretentious, didactic. You have nothing to do with children, you don't know them. She wasn't fascinated – just shy, polite; even scared of you. You must have said something that made him do it. You didn't like him, you only liked the sister. Didn't you?

MacAlistair, he'd cluck, shake his head, thinking Crick exaggerates: 'You shouldn't take it so hard, man.'

'I know. I know,' Crick had said. 'I should be ashamed of myself.' And so for a week now he'd come docilely to this same spot each day, MacAlistair's prescription, cultivating solitude and self-sufficiency; sat in this crab's-claw of rock, solemnly watching gulls, believing that this was good in itself and good for him ...

He never even heard him till he was almost on him, crunching up in his glossy two-tone shoes to stand over Crick, panting and dangerous – 'You hit my boy. You cunt, stand up.'

Crick got to his feet, stumbling back, and the man pushed him in the chest. 'Well I'll tell you what, mate, *I'm* going to hit *you* now. *And*' – he pushed him again, and Crick put his arms up in front of his face to shield himself – 'I'm going to have damages off of you. You broke his tooth right off!'

'I beg your pardon,' flinching, 'but I did not hit your child.'

'You fucking did. You fucking educated ponce.' The ferocity in his voice was not far from a sob, and Crick saw what his child's broken tooth had done to this man, and that he was as frightened of what was happening as Crick was himself. He glared at Crick with blue eyes bloodshot with aggression, but his face was pink and his mouth beneath a soft blond moustache gulped in distress. He reached to push Crick again, but then let his arm fall by his side as if his adrenalin had failed him. He was squarely built, and all his clothes had a brand-newness that was bathetic on that dour beach. 'You fucking bastard!' he said, and looked aside, short and bewildered.

'I'm sorry, I really am sorry what happened to your son, but I didn't touch him'; guiltily thankful that it was true.

'He says you did.' He glanced up at Crick almost pleading for his anger back, indisputable righteous anger.

'What does the little girl say?'

'She won't say anything. She says she don't know.' He looked over his shoulder as if his conduct was being watched, and steadied his voice to a sneer: 'And how do you reckon he did it, then?'

'I'm afraid he threw a stone at a bird – a ringed plover that we were watching. I was running after him to try to stop him and he fell.'

'Just fell, eh? Hard enough to break his tooth off!' The man gave him the lie, his face tilted in an attitude Crick knew: but he saw he was believed. That the boy would stone a bird raised no query with his father. But the broken tooth – he could not get that back for him; and now not even the futile consolation of revenge, tooth for a tooth, was allowed him. He faced Crick baffled, his blunt hands hanging, searching for a gap. Crick knew it was there, and he shifted his footing on the stones as the man saw it too: 'But why were you – what were you doing messing with my kids anyway? What right have you . . . ?'

Astonishingly he tailed off. He stood staring at Crick's chest, so that Crick slowly felt himself diffused into a middle distance of educated ponces; and then as if in answer to this very notion he said, 'What's the use? What's the fucking use?', shrugging; and now Crick had watched all of the family exit right, round the broken cliff-end to some place beyond, a yokel in-law's farmyard or field, where sat their motor-home, all the comfort, ownership and status that could be amassed on four wheels.

A gull high overhead uttered a single empty cry. The light was going, the tide had covered the sand again and was butting at the stones, sending up spurts of spray that pattered down like hail. Crick looked up shivering at the bird, realizing that he always thought of them as cold-blooded. Presumably pterodactyls were; the blood had warmed over millions of years, in the evolution from scales to feathers. The gull looked down on nothing that a pterodactyl might not have seen – except for Crick, and suddenly he couldn't get away from the place fast enough. He hurried to the cliff path that led towards MacAlistair's cottage, leaving the cove without a last look back.

He drove out the cold with oversweetened tea and a fry-up of sausages, eggs, bacon, baked beans, canned tomatoes. But the agitation of the afternoon wouldn't leave him. He had bouts of shivering, fear and tension left over from that animal confrontation; and as he packed his holdall and tidied up the house he could not close his mind on the bull-like man carrying away his unappeased anger in defence of his young. The boy too, snarling through reddened teeth, still racked him between revulsion and remorse.

Tomorrow the customary remedies, he thought: oh well, what difference does it make?

And the pub having only the one bar, there was no retreating: they saw him the moment he pushed open the door. 'Evening,' he said to the publican. 'Pint of heavy, please. Pardon? Oh, yes, pinched an extra day.' He could feel their stare on his back. They were at a table between the curtained window and the fire, looking, it occurred to him, as if they'd been cut out of a mail-order catalogue.

He took a grip on his pint, turned, and walked across the bar to them. 'Will you let me get you a drink?' he asked. His voice managed diffidence and concern without being conciliatory, but he was holding on to the back of a chair to keep his equilibrium.

'We've got drinks,' the man said slowly. 'But you can sit down if you want.'

'My name's David Crick,' said Crick.

'How d'you do.' He sat back, making himself slightly jowly. Can't be more than thirty, Crick thought: so a father by the time he was twenty. The wife had a glass of vodka and tonic in front of her, and her fingers kept hold of the stem. Unexpectedly she spoke first. 'What do you want, then?'

Good question, he thought wryly. 'I wanted to know ... Look – I'm as upset as you are about Grant's ... about what happened.'

'Oh, you are? Then why did you do it?'

'I actually didn't do it. I did not do anything to your son.'

The man said: 'You might not of hit him or pushed him, but if you hadn't of chased after him like that –?'

'You know why I chased after him?'

'You told me he was chucking a stone at this bird.'

'Well, wouldn't you agree that he shouldn't be allowed to do that?'

'Suppose he shouldn't, I'm not that bothered. Didn't you do a few things when you were a boy his age? I suppose *you* didn't? ... You reckon that deserved having one of his front teeth smashed out?'

'About his tooth I really am sorry, please believe me. What can I say?'

'You can't say anything,' the woman broke in. 'What *I* want to know is, what exactly you were *up* to with my children. I'm not satisfied, not at all. What do you think you're doing, coming up to little children on the beach? With this binoculars and all that? What's your game?'

'In the first place, I didn't come up to them, they came up to me. Katherine asked if she could look through my binoculars, and then the second time, as far as I can make out, she brought Grant along so that he could have a go too.' The obscene finger pointed, Crick found that he was not afraid after all; or only enough to make him pompous. 'I hope you can be satisfied with that, can you? Katherine seems to me an extremely nice and intelligent child. It was a pleasure to tell her a little about the birds, and I think it was a pleasure to her to learn.'

The man sat forward, setting his forearms on the wooden table with a thump. 'But not Grant! You didn't think Grant was a nice, intelligent child? I bet you thought Grant was a right little bugger, didn't you? just because he didn't reckon your precious bloody birds! I bet when you saw what happened to him you said serve the bastard right! – a little kid of ten with his tooth broke off. Eh, didn't you?'

They were both coming at him. 'He's above average, is Grant,' the woman was saying, and she rapped Crick's hand with her fingernail for attention. 'He's an above average child.'

The man kept his forefinger pointed in Crick's face, glaring along it. 'You let me tell you a few things about that kid you don't think much of. He can programme a computer – can you programme a computer? He mended my watch for me, all by himself. He's built an electric speedboat with remote control that does thirty knots. He's invented his own burglar alarm system – my whole house is fitted up with it. Matter of fact the application's in at the patents office now: I drew it up with him. That's not bad for a kid of ten – or don't you think so?'

His wife took it up: 'He's got his own television in his room, that he rebuilt himself. It was one the proper telly engineer gave up as hopeless – couldn't get a flicker out of it.'

Crick sat looking from one to the other, fleetingly conscious that the astonishment on his face could be no less than they'd wish. They were handing out a bit of enlightenment, while getting their prodigy his due. Relishing the task, the man had shelved his anger and become expansive.

'Well, with his telly I gave him a hand to begin with – being an electrical engineer myself, y'know; and I don't do bad – but by the end I'm telling you he knew things I didn't.

'T'other day, *he* was explaining to *me* some bit about radio telescopes. Drawing diagrams and all that. He does drawings all the time, Grant. Racing cars, spaceships – all technically correct, mind: I asked his science teacher myself and he said so. We've got one big drawing he did up on the sitting-room wall, framed, "City of the Future" he calls it. It's got moving pavements, air-conditioning indoors and out, heliport, sportsdrome, videophones, crime prevention, space station – you wouldn't believe all the details he's put into it. Marvellous.' Turned almost affable, he got up and went to the bar.

His wife, still hostile, watched Crick as he tried to find something adequate to say. 'You think we're ignorant people, don't you? Well, *we* might not have the education, but we want the best for our children and they're going to get it ... Everything they need, they get. Books, equipment. Tape recorder. And we encourage them, that's what counts, you know, the encouragement every day. Grant'll go to the university; and in a few years he'll be able to name his price. I know.'

Her husband came back with drinks. 'Here,' he said, 'what was the name of it – your poxy bird on the beach?'

'A ringed plover.'

'Yeah. Well, I wouldn't know a ringed plover from an oven-ready chicken!'

They all laughed, the man watching Crick with sidelong spite.

'No, seriously,' – showing willing to persevere with Crick, talk a little sense into him – 'seriously, all that nature stuff. You make such a fuss about it, but is it necessary? I mean, if that's what you care about, well and good, that's your problem; but take my son Grant. With *his* abilities. Want to know my opinion, it'd be a waste – I mean that, a serious waste – if he was to spend his time *bird*watching. See, you've got to look *ahead*, you've got to consider what the world needs. Things like the computer, the laser beam ... that sort of amazing discoveries, they're what the future's all about. Only more so. Electronics, technology, space travel, nuclear physics. That's the stuff you've got to get into if you're going to get somewhere. And I'll tell you now,' folding his arms, 'that boy is.'

'Well, fair enough,' Crick said feebly, as the landlord rang the bell for time, 'but – surely you'd agree that if there's pleasure to be had from observing other living things –'

'That's just it,' the woman interrupted, '*if* there's pleasure. *If* that's what you like. But Grant doesn't like. He's happy when he's using his hands, using his brain. He's got a right to choose what he wants to do, hasn't he? He hasn't *got* to be interested in your old birds, has he? ringed plovers or whatever! If he isn't. And you can see darned well he isn't, he couldn't have made it much clearer, could he?'

'And here's something else for you,' the man said. 'All the people there are in the world now, well, they can still all watch the box. That's probably why it's there. But suppose all of 'em went down to the beach to look at birds – there wouldn't be room on the beach for any birds for them to look at! So maybe it's just as well for you. How about that?'

('Time, please, you folks,' said the landlord.)

'It's a point,' Crick admitted.

The man put his arm round his wife's shoulders as they went out. 'Night,' he said. Condescending to a chastised adversary.

By ten the next morning Crick had a hundred miles behind him. Except that it was slowing him down on the winding road, he took no notice at first of the big burnished-aluminium van. The children must have been staring back at him for minutes before he noticed. Side by

side, not speaking, the small pale faces gazed down, swayed gently by
the vehicle's cushiony suspension. Crick could see the split in the boy's
lip, still puffy, but his eyes merely looked back neutral and unblinking.
Poor kid, Crick thought; and then: is he forbidding me to feel anything
for him, or daring me to?

Yet her face, grave and tranquil beside her brother's, told him no
more – confided nothing. If the road would only stop twisting and let
him get past.

One of his parents must have called back to the boy: he turned away
to look out of the nearside window. In the distance was the sea, flinty
beneath a travelling sky, and offshore an enormous rig was under
construction, a triangulated mass of struts and stanchions rearing from
the water. Crick gave it a couple of quick glances; even from here the
livid pricking of welding torches was visible against the clouds. The girl
had joined her brother; and now, looking across once more, Crick saw,
nearer but still a great way off, light from the hidden sun glint in mid air
– glint, pivot and go out – diffracted off the wings of a host of gulls
wheeling together, sprung from their mudflat to scream and settle back.
And as they did the little girl looked back quickly to see if he had seen.

Crick smiled, shifting down to pass, and the van grew smaller in his
rear-view mirror.

MORE ABOUT PENGUINS, PELICANS
AND PUFFINS

For further information about books available from Penguins please write to
Dept EP, Penguin Books Ltd, Harmondsworth, Middlesex UB7 ODA.

In the U.S.A.: For a complete list of books available from Penguins in the
United States write to Dept DG, Penguin Books, 299 Murray Hill Parkway,
East Rutherford, New Jersey 07073.

In Canada: For a complete list of books available from Penguins in Canada
write to Penguin Books Canada Ltd, 2801 John Street, Markham, Ontario
L3R 1B4.

In Australia: For a complete list of books available from Penguins in Australia
write to the Marketing Department, Penguin Books Australia Ltd, P.O. Box
257, Ringwood, Victoria 3134.

In New Zealand: For a complete list of books available from Penguins in New
Zealand write to the Marketing Department, Penguin Books (N.Z.) Ltd, P.O.
Box 4019, Auckland 10.

In India: For a complete list of books available from Penguins in India write
to Penguin Overseas Ltd, 706 Eros Apartments, 56 Nehru Place, New Delhi
110019.

FIREBIRD 1

Edited by T. J. Binding

'This first annual round-up of current prose writing boasts a discarded fragment by Graham Greene, a fine, garrulous story by Salman Rushdie, post-structuralist brilliance by Adam Mars-Jones ... There are memorable individual pieces and an impressive range. The anthology will help readers keep an eye on what is most serious in new fiction' – *Sunday Times*

'Excellent ... One of the brightest publishing ideas in years ... work by a wide range of writers, each with something very different to say' – *Glasgow Herald*

'A fascinating collection ... full of pleasurable and imaginative images ... essential reading for anyone who is interested in new writing' – *In Dublin*

Contributors to *Firebird 1* are:

Ron Butlin	Helen Harris	Adam Mars-Jones
A. S. Byatt	Dermot Healy	Salman Rushdie
Angela Carter	Desmond Hogan	Victor Sage
Jack Debney	James Kelman	Clive Sinclair
Douglas Dunn	James Lasdun	Jonathan Steffen
Alasdair Gray	Brian McCabe	Graham Swift
Graham Greene	Bernard Mac Laverty	William Trevor

FIREBIRD 2

Edited by T. J. Binding

'Brave as well as exciting ... a forum for both new and established talent' – *Books and Bookmen*

In *Firebird 2* the contributors are:

James Campbell	Paul R. Hyde	Francis Stuart
Meira Chand	Kazuo Ishiguro	Alan Temperley
A. E. Ellis	James Kelman	Dai Vaughan
M. J. Fitzgerald	R. M. Lamming	Fay Weldon
Roy A. K. Heath	Victor Power	Angus Wilson
Alan Hollinghurst	Dyan Sheldon	